Medical Frontiers and Jewish Law

Essays and Responsa

STUDIES IN PROGRESSIVE HALAKHAH
General Editor: Walter Jacob
Solomon B. Freehof Institute of Progressive Halakhah.
www.Jewish-Law-Institute.com

Walter Jacob and Moshe Zemer (eds.) DYNAMIC JEWISH LAW
Progressive Halakhah - Essence and Application

Walter Jacob and Moshe Zemer (eds.) RABBINIC – LAY RELATIONS
IN JEWISH LAW

Walter Jacob and Moshe Zemer (eds.) CONVERSION TO JUDAISM
IN JEWISH LAW - Essays and Responsa

Walter Jacob and Moshe Zemer (eds.) DEATH AND EUTHANASIA
IN JEWISH LAW - Essays and Responsa

Walter Jacob and Moshe Zemer (eds.) THE FETUS AND FERTILITY
IN JEWISH LAW - Essays and Responsa

Walter Jacob and Moshe Zemer (eds.) ISRAEL AND THE DIASPORA
IN JEWISH LAW - Essays and Responsa

Walter Jacob and Moshe Zemer (eds.) AGING AND THE AGED
IN JEWISH LAW - Essays and Responsa

Walter Jacob and Moshe Zemer (eds.) MARRIAGE AND ITS OBSTACLES
IN JEWISH LAW - Essays and Responsa

Walter Jacob and Moshe Zemer (eds.) CRIME AND PUNISHMENT
IN JEWISH LAW - Essays and Responsa

Walter Jacob and Moshe Zemer (eds.) GENDER ISSUES IN JEWISH LAW
Essays and Responsa

Walter Jacob and Moshe Zemer (eds.) RE-EXAMINING JEWISH LAW
Essays and Responsa

Walter Jacob and Moshe Zemer (eds.) THE ENVIRONMENT IN JEWISH LAW
Essays and Responsa

Walter Jacob (ed.) BEYOND THE LETTER OF THE LAW
Essays in Honor of Moshe Zemer

Walter Jacob (ed.) with Moshe Zemer SEXUAL ISSUES IN JEWISH LAW
Essays and Responsa

Walter Jacob (ed.) with Moshe Zemer POVERTY AND TZEDAKAH IN JEWISH LAW
Essays and Responsa

Walter Jacob (ed.) NAPOLEON'S INFLUENCE ON JEWISH LAW
The Sanhedrin of 1807 and its Modern Consequences

Walter Jacob (ed.) ONLY IN AMERICA
The Open Society and Jewish Law

Walter Jacob (ed.) WAR AND TERRORISM IN JEWISH LAW
Essays and Response

Walter Jacob (ed.) MEDICAL FRONTIERS AND JEWISH LAW
Essays and Responsa

MEDICAL FRONTIERS IN JEWISH LAW

Essays and Responsa

Edited by

Walter Jacob

Solomon B. Freehof Institute of Progressive Jewish Law
Rodef Shalom Press
Pittsburgh, Pennsylvania

The Solomon B. Freehof Institute of Progressive Jewish Law was established in 1989 to honor Dr. Freehof's memory and his enduring contributions to the development of the *Halakhah*.

Published by the Rodef Shalom Press
4905 Fifth Avenue
Pittsburgh, Pensylvania
U.S.A.

Library of Congress-in-publication-data

Jacob, Walter 1930-

ISBN 0-929699-24-6

Dedicated to

Nancy Berkowitz

in

Friendship and Gratitude

ACKNOWLEDGMENTS

The Freehof Institute of Progressive Halakhah again expresses its gratitude to the Rodef Shalom Congregation for its support in technical matters connected with this volume. Our thanks once more to Hanna Gruen and Irene Jacob for their help with early version of this book.

Our special thanks to Nancy Berkowitz whose careful copy-editing has improved not only this volume, but also many of its predecessors through the last decade. In gratitude we dedicate this volume to her.

CONTENTS

INTRODUCTION

Medicine continues to advance at a remarkable speed; the changes raise ethical issues, especially as the science of genetics breaks new ground. The use of these advances, their risks and unknown side-effects bring new problems. Finally the question of access to medical advances raises thorny issues. These and a host of other difficult problems were the topic of several seminars of the Institute of Progressive Halakhah.

The papers and the responsa here presented deal with philosophical and practical issues as seen from the perspective of Liberal Jewish *halakhah*. They seek to add another set of voices to the continuing public debate on these questions.Unfortunately, not all those who presented papers were able to provide them in a more extensive form for publication. The result is a much more restricted volume than originally planned; we will visit these and other related issues again.

THE WOODCHOPPER REVISITED
ON ANALOGY, *HALAKHAH*, AND JEWISH BIOETHICS
Mark Washofsky

Two decades have elapsed since the appearance of Louis Newman's article titled "Woodchoppers and Respirators: The Problem of Interpretation in Contemporary Jewish Ethics."[1] The essay has been frequently cited, and rightly so. It deserves mention in particular because it is one of the earliest efforts to apply developments in recent Anglo-American legal theory to help elucidate "the problem of interpretation" of Jewish legal texts. That problem, simply stated, is this: legal texts do not interpret themselves, nor do they usually admit of a single determinate meaning. Despite this fact, many jurists and Jewish ethicists write as though the texts they study do contain such meaning and that the task of the interpreter/exegete is to isolate and extract it, drawing upon the writings of such legal and literary theorists as Terrance Sandalow,[2] Paul Brest,[3] James Boyd White,[4] Stanley Fish,[5] Owen Fiss,[6] Karl Llewellyn,[7] and Ronald Dworkin.[8]

Newman argues that "the meaning of a text lies less in the words themselves than in the interpretive framework the exegete brings to them."[9] Jewish ethicists, therefore, should beware of speaking in the name of "Judaism," as in "Judaism teaches that...." Rather, they should adopt a more nuanced style that reflects the nature of the interpretive process: the Jewish view on a particular ethical issue is "what we, given our particular interpretive assumptions and our particular way of construing the coherence of the tradition as a whole, find within the traditional sources."[10]

Newman uses these theoretical insights to analyze and critique the writings of a number of Jewish ethicists concerning the treatment of the terminally ill. As is the case with the discussion of most ethical issues, this one is textual and interpretive in nature: the Jewish ethicist identifies a set of texts in traditional Jewish literature that are relevant to her topic and then interprets them in order to derive an answer or answers to the problem she is addressing. In this particular case, one of the most prominent of these "relevant" texts is *Shulchan Arukh Yoreh Deah* 339:1, which lists the actions that one is permitted and forbidden to undertake with respect to the *goses*, a dying person whose death is considered imminent. The *goses*, the text tells us, is considered a living person in all legal respects. It is forbidden, therefore, to take any action that might cause him to die more quickly, since such an action is tantamount to bloodshed. On the other hand, it is permissible to remove from the scene a factor defined as an impediment to his death, such as the sound made by a woodchopper doing his work (hence, the title of Newman's article). A number of Jewish ethicists see this text, among others, as a precedent for the contemporary bioethical question of euthanasia, particularly the familiar distinction between "active" euthanasia ("mercy killing," assisted suicide; positive actions taken to hasten the patient's death) and "passive" euthanasia [discontinuation of futile medical treatment]; "allowing nature to take its course," etc.).[11] As Newman sees it, this move–from the text to its contemporary application–is seriously problematic, for at least two reasons. First, as indicated, the text addresses the specific example of the *goses*, whose death will in all likelihood occur within 72 hours,[12] and it is not obvious that its conclusion would apply as well to patients considered terminally ill but who are not at this moment in the throes of death. Second, it is also not obvious that the "impediments" spoken of in the *Shulchan Arukh* – the woodchopper and the rest – are substantially akin to the panoply of technologies utilized nowadays in the treatment of the terminally ill. The latter are classified as "medical" whereas the former never enjoyed that designation; what then can this text teach us concerning the ethics of the contemporary medical situation? For Newman, this disconnect between the text and the (varying) lessons that Jewish ethicists tend to draw from it is symptomatic of the larger theoretical issue he explores in his article. Traditional texts do not *necessarily* prove the conclusions are derived from them; indeed, it is misleading to say that these conclusions are "derived" at all, as though they lay at the end of a process of logical or scientific reasoning that identifies the one true meaning of the source(s) at hand. The conclusions, rather, cannot be imagined in the absence of the interpretive assumptions the ethicists bring to their reading of the texts. "I would propose that contemporary Jewish ethics be conceived not as an attempt to determine what past authorities would say about contemporary problems if they were alive today, but as a dialectical relation in which finally no sharp distinction can be made between our voices and theirs…. Any reading of the texts that we produce, and any conclusions we draw from them, are as much our work as theirs."[13]

Newman's article is important in a number of ways. It is, as I indicated earlier, one of the first efforts to integrate the work of contemporary legal theorists into the study of halakhic texts, an approach that greatly contributes to our understanding of Jewish legal thought and the halakhic process.[14] It is also exemplary of the scholarly direction called the "interpretive turn" – the recognition of "the importance of interpretation in all inquiry"[15] – that has characterized the humanities and social sciences for more than a generation. Practitioners of a number of disciplines have moved away from the old positivist model of study that idealizes the objective analysis of empirical data and toward an approach that emphasizes that all reason is rooted in history, tradition, and human experience. Hence the observer, even the "hard" scientist,[16] cannot know an object or explain his data without interpreting them; "all understanding is interpretation,"[17] a process that is not *wertfrei* but always proceeds from a contingent and historical position, the framework of practices, interests, and problems within which one lives, works, and thinks. Newman's presentation helps us to see the activity of Jewish law as an ongoing interpretive (hermeneutical) process that attempts to arrive at a constructive understanding of the *halakhah* through argument rather than an effort, akin to scientific method, to deduce the single correct answer from the data. Finally, and with specific reference to our topic here, Newman challenges the way in which many thinkers pursue the enterprise of Jewish bioethics. To cite sources as precedents without asking what makes them precedential, to rely upon analogies without acknowledging that one is operating from within a previously constructed interpretive framework that dictates both the analogies and the meaning to be drawn from them – these things smack of unreflective habit rather than a careful, self-aware methodology. This challenge is a good thing, because no scholar, whether "traditional" or "academic," should pursue her work in an unreflective manner.

But what if the challenge proves to be too much of a good thing? Could it be that Newman's critique does more than simply call upon writers in the field of Jewish bioethics to examine their interpretive assumptions? Is it possible that his observations undermine the very enterprise of Jewish bioethics? Much of that enterprise has operated within the field of *halakhah* and Jewish legal thought. Scholars investigating the question "what does Judaism say?" about a particular issue relating to medical practice have followed the standard methodologies of Jewish law, combing the corpus of authoritative halakhic texts for sources that, through the application of analogical reasoning, might serve as precedents that offer possible answers to their question. This legal (perhaps a better term is "judicial") methodology characterizes the work of liberal[18] as well as Orthodox halakhists as well as of those academic scholars whose work has been described, inaccurately, as "nonhalakhic."[19] Newman, to be sure, does not advocate the abandonment of this traditional, text-based approach to Jewish bioethics, even as he calls upon those who engage in it to do so with care and intellectual self-awareness.[20] Yet, since the publication of his article, a number of critiques have taken aim at precisely this approach and on very similar grounds.[21] The authors of these critiques tend to work from liberal Jewish perspectives;[22] for that reason, and for the sake of convenience, I will call them "the liberal critics." Their objections, though varied, coalesce around the assertion that traditional modes of halakhic thinking, based upon analogy, precedent, and something called– imprecisely – "halakhic formalism"[23] are inadequate to the task of contemporary Jewish bioethics. The texts, they contend, provide an insufficient basis from which to extrapolate meaning for today's Jew who confronts a brave new world of medical choices and dilemmas. The analogies are forced, artificial, and morally irrelevant. Moreover, the traditional Jewish activity of deriving guidance from authoritative texts simply fails to capture that which is essentially "human" and "ethical" in Judaism's teachings concerning the practice of medicine. This attack carries some serious implications for those of us who work in the field of progressive *halakhah*, for it suggests that our approach to bioethical questions, an approach firmly rooted in the discipline of traditional halakhic thinking as taught and practiced by our teacher R. Solomon B. Freehof, is not sufficiently progressive or, for that matter, ethical. My goal here is to examine these criticisms in both a general and a specific light. In general, I want to discuss the pivotal role of analogy in traditional legal and halakhic reasoning. Specifically, I want to consider how analogy has served halakhists, both Orthodox and progressive, in their efforts to confront the difficult life-and-death issues surrounding the treatment of the terminally ill. The findings, I think, will reveal both the strengths and weaknesses of the traditional case-and-text-based approach in *halakhah* as it relates to contemporary bioethical questions, and they will also reveal that the strengths outweigh the weaknesses. That is to say, the method of analogy, when used in the way it ought to be used, can lead the progressive halakhist to bioethical conclusions both progressive *and* ethical. I will argue that progressive halakhists, as long as they heed Newman's call to examine their interpretive assumptions and make them clear, need not reject the traditional methodologies to create a progressive Jewish bioethic. On the contrary: Jewish bioethics, even of the progressive variety, is best understood and practiced as a subspecialty within the discipline of *halakhah*.

I. *Analogy in Law and Ethics.* There is no question that analogy, the process of reasoning by cases or by examples, plays a pivotal role in the work of lawyers and judges. Some scholars go so far as to deem analogy (or casuistry, as it is sometimes called) *the* distinctive method of legal reasoning.[24] Others recognize it as one mode of reasoning, albeit an important one, out of a number of modes that jurists customarily employ.[25] It is essentially a four-step process, beginning with the identification of a problem or target case (*B*), that is, a situation that requires an answer or solution. Step two is to find a base-point or source case (*A*), a case that has previously been decided and that seems to be an appropriate starting point from which to reason and to analyze the problem or target case. In step three, one points out the respects in which the problem or target case is similar to the base-point case as well as the respects in which the two cases differ. Step four, finally, requires that one determine whether the two cases are sufficiently similar so that the solution or answer reached in the base-point case should apply to the problem case as well or that they are sufficiently different so that the solution to the earlier case does not apply to the case at hand. In legal terminology, one argues that case *A* either serves or does not serve as a suitable precedent for case *B*, so that, on the basis of the principle that like cases ought to be treated alike, the solution to *A* should (or should not) control our response to *B*.

The phrase "legal terminology" raises an important theoretical issue. We say that analogy is a mode of something called *legal reasoning*, an approach to analysis presumably unique to the community of jurists and the practice of law, yet we recognize that this form of reasoning is precisely the way we think about and analyze many problems we encounter in everyday life. To take but one example:[26] Mother allows older brother to stay up until 9:00 p.m., and younger brother seeks the same treatment (step one). Younger brother argues (step two) that the rule governing older brother's bedtime (*A*) is a source-case for his own issue (*B*), the problem case. He does so (step three) by pointing to the similarities between him and older brother: both are children in the same family, and this shared factor suggests that the two should receive equal treatment in the form of the same bedtime rule. For her part in step three, mother questions the analogy, arguing that there is a significant difference between the two cases: older children need less sleep than younger children. In step four, mother determines that the difference is more important than the similarity. The analogical reasoning process employed in this family setting is much the same as that employed in law, with the exception, of course, that legal argument is more formal and stylized.[27] This perception, in turn, raises the question whether "legal reasoning" is at all a distinct form of reasoning or simply the application of general forms of reasoning within a specifically legal context.[28]

In any event, lawyers do resort to analogy and precedent in order to extend the accepted understandings of the law to cover new cases that offer similar, though not identical, circumstances. Consider the following problem case (step one): are wiretapping and electronic surveillance undertaken by law-enforcement agencies permissible in the absence of a judicially issued warrant? This was the question put before the U.S. Supreme Court in the1928 case *Olmstead v. United States*.[29] Olmstead was a bootlegger convicted on the basis of evidence gathered through a wiretap placed by Federal officials who had not obtained a warrant to do so. He contended (step two) that the wiretap violated the Fourth Amendment of the U.S. Constitution, which provides: "The right of the people to be secure in their persons, houses, papers, and effects, against unreasonable searches and seizures shall not be violated; and no Warrant shall issue but upon probable cause... particularly describing the place to be searched and the persons or things to be seized." In steps three and four, both the majority of the court and the dissenters offer analogical arguments as to whether the analogy is successful: is the Fourth Amendment an appropriate source from which to derive the rule that governs this case? Writing for the court's majority, Chief Justice William Howard Taft declared that the circumstances of this case were fundamentally dissimilar from those provided for by the relevant constitutional text:[30]

The amendment itself shows that the search is to be of material things–the person, the house, his papers, or his effects. The description of the warrant necessary to make the proceeding lawful is that it must specify the place to be searched and the person or things to be seized.... The amendment does not forbid what was done here. There was no searching. There was no seizure. The evidence was secured by the use of the sense of hearing and that only. There was no entry of the houses or offices of the defendants. By the invention of the telephone 50 years ago, and its application for the purpose of extending communications, one can talk with another at a far distant place. The language of the amendment cannot be extended and expanded to include telephone wires reaching to the whole world from the defendant's house or office. The intervening wires are not part of his house or office any more than are the highways along which they are stretched.

In dissent, meanwhile, Justice Louis Brandeis rejected this understanding of the Fourth Amendment as overly literal. The specific examples the amendment mentions are to be understood in light of its general purpose. When the text was adopted, to be sure, "force and violence" – the invasion of a person's private domain – were the only means by which the government could seize evidence from him without his consent. "But 'time works changes, brings into existence new conditions and purposes.'[31] Subtler and more far-reaching means of invading privacy have become available to the government. Discovery and invention have made it possible for the government, by means far more effective than stretching upon the rack, to obtain disclosure in court of what is whispered in the closet."[32] In other words, said Brandeis, the Fourth Amendment *is* a valid source case from which to draw the analogy, because the essential similarities between it and the problem case outweigh the material differences between them.

Both the informal example sketched above and the opinions in the *Olmstead* case suggest the strengths and relative advantages of analogical reasoning over deductive reasoning, thinking that begins with general principles and thereupon moves to solve specific cases. One of these strengths is the power of analogy to promote consensus in matters involving legal, ethical, or political disagreement. People who differ over broad, general principles might nonetheless be able to come together over specifics. "[I]n the face of persistent disagreement or uncertainty about what morality generally requires, people can reason about particular cases by reference to analogies. They point to cases in which their judgments are firm. They proceed from those firm judgments to the more difficult ones. This is how judges often operate; it is also how ordinary people tend to think."[33] Suppose, for example, that we were to approach either of our two exemplary cases (bedtime rules and wiretapping) on the basis of deductive reasoning. We would first have to affirm, as our major premise, either of two controversial principles: a commitment to a "lenient" or a "strict" theory of parenting, or a commitment to one side or the other of the age-old debate between the right of the individual to privacy and the responsibility of the government to protect the community. It would be difficult in either case to resolve the dispute between the principles or to identify the theoretical happy medium or point of balance between them. It would be simpler and surer, however, to come to consensus on specific problematic instances by working from examples over which we have already reached agreement. This is perhaps another way of expressing the insight that broad, general principles tend to be useless in resolving legal and moral controversies.

Albert Jonsen and Stephen Toulmin stress this point in their vigorous defense of casuistry, or reasoning from particulars in the discipline of ethics.[34] Although people tend to think of general principles as the whole of ethical discourse, this is a drastic oversimplification of the state of affairs. "Taken by themselves, the *general* rules and maxims that play a part in people's ethical deliberations are only rarely matters of serious dispute.... On the contrary, it is just those situations that are *not* covered by appeal to any single simple rule that begin to be problematic; and in just those cases our concern to act rightly gives rise to genuinely moral 'questions' and 'issues' [emphasis in original]."[35] Generalizations, in other words, are empty of substantive content beyond the obvious and uncontroversial examples – cases – which gave rise to them in the first place. Once we move past those obvious areas of agreement to the more difficult (and interesting) questions of morality and ethics, it is only through the application of casuistry, the identification of similarities and differences between types of example, that moral thought can productively proceed. Rules are important, even essential, but it is by considering examples – that is, through casuistry and analogical reasoning – that we determine just what those rules cover and how far they extend.[36] Such an approach, which Jonsen and Toulmin attribute to such distinguished contemporary writers as Michael Walzer and Sissela Bok, "is wholly consistent with our moral practice."[37] On the other hand, analogical thinking has its weaknesses, too. The most obvious of these lies in step four of our description of the process of analogy, the determination that the similarities between the two cases outweigh or do not outweigh the differences between them. This raises the "problem of importance": how exactly do we evaluate the relative legal or moral significance of the similarities and differences?[38] Analogical reasoning does not by itself solve this problem. It can suggest possible precedents, but it cannot assure us that these prior decisions are *in fact* precedential, because *that* decision must rest with the interpreter. "At most, analogical thinking can give rise to a judgment about probabilities, and these are of uncertain magnitude."[39] Unlike deductive reasoning, in which the conclusion is said to follow logically from the premises, analogy cannot make a methodological, quasi-mathematical claim for the validity of its conclusions. It rather *suggests* its conclusion, the correctness of which must therefore be *argued* by its advocate on the basis of something other than formal demonstration. All of this is reminiscent of the famous remark of Justice Oliver Wendell Holmes, Jr.: "General propositions do not decide concrete cases. The decision will depend on a judgment or intuition more subtle than any articulate major premise."[40] In dealing with issues of moral or legal import, it is rare that we proceed from a general concept to the solution of a specific case, for the applicability of that concept to the case is itself a matter of analogical reasoning.[41] (How do we know that principle *X* covers case *Y* unless we have already identified the similarities between them?) Yet that reasoning itself requires a *judgment* of the relative importance of those similarities. And such judgment, by its nature, is not determined by logical necessity. Some theorists, to be sure, make a stronger claim for analogy, namely that it is a "valid" (and not merely "probable") approach to truth in that its conclusions are supported by the professional skills and craft virtues of those who employ it.[42] This notion strikes me as excessively mystical,[43] an all-too-sure confidence in the capacity of the jurist or the ethicist to make correct inferences. The very fact that analogical inference involves an act of the imagination (one "sees" or intuits a potential similarity between cases and then tests that intuition) suggests that we should be careful about speaking of its "validity," a term more suited to deductive analysis. The weaker claim, at any rate, is more easily defended. Analogy is a necessary and ubiquitous element of human reasoning, but it requires an act of judgment on the part of its advocate in order to prove its point. That judgment, to win wide acceptance, will necessarily draw upon the advocate's educated sense of what the relevant interpretive community will generally hold to be the correct legal or ethical resolution of the case. Such is perhaps the best that anyone can do in the field of legal or ethical reasoning, and for that reason, the conclusion will probably pass the test of legitimacy: that is, the interpretive community will accept it as a legitimate (if not the *only* legitimate) answer to the question. It remains, however, a *judgment;* it does not enjoy the status of demonstrable proof.[44]

II. *Analogy in Halakhah*. Given that *halakhah*, traditional Jewish law, displays the characteristics of both law and ethics,[45] it should not be surprising that analogy plays a major role in halakhic thinking. Any discussion of that role must distinguish between two major subject areas. The first of these concerns the extent to which the sages, the rabbis of the formative era of rabbinic Judaism, included analogy among their "hermeneutical principles" (*midot she-hatorah nidreshet bahen*), which served them in linking the content of the Oral Torah to the verses of the Written Torah. The various listings of these principles contain forms of comparison (*hekesh, kal vachomer, binyav av*) that can be termed "analogical," although the precise characterization of each of them has long been a matter of controversy.[46] My concern here is not with these talmudic-midrashic *midot* but with the second large subject area: the use of analogy by rabbis in the Talmud and in the post-talmudic period as a means of learning the law in new cases by reasoning from already decided cases or rules. The term for this sort of analogical thinking is *ledamoyei milta lemilta*, "to compare one thing to another." The ability to employ analogy to derive answers to new and difficult questions is considered central to the activity of halakhic scholarship and to the very conception of a rabbinical sage.[47] At the same time, as we shall see, halakhic authorities express a distinct wariness over the process, out of concern that its unchecked or improper use can lead to mistaken conclusions. Rabbinical discussion of analogical reasoning tends to begin with a *baraita* in B. *Bava Batra* 130b: One should not derive the *halakhah* either from theoretical learning (*limud* [48]) or from a ruling in an actual case (*maaseh*) until one is instructed that "this *halakhah* is to be followed in an actual case (*halakhah lemaaseh*)." If one asks and is told "this is *halakhah lemaaseh*," one may apply that ruling in an actual case, as long as one does not draw an analogy (between cases; *uvilvad she-lo yedameh*), The thrust of this text, as it is generally explained,[49] is that each of these methods of learning is afflicted with defects that can be corrected only when the two are combined. A student should not draw practical halakhic conclusions from his teacher's theoretical discussion of the law, for were the teacher to consider an actual case rather than to speculate in abstraction, he might well study the issues more carefully and rule differently. The student should also beware of learning from his teacher's decisions in case, lest he mistake the teacher's reasoning for the decision and then go on to apply the same ruling, incorrectly, to another case. The student may follow the teacher's theory or decision only when he has been told that "yes, this is the theory of the law, and you may rely on it in matters of practice." The *baraita*'s concluding caveat – "so long as one does not draw an analogy" – puzzles the *setam Talmud* (*i.e.*, the anonymous editor[s] of the passage), which objects: "We use the entire Torah for the purpose of analogy (*veha kol hatorah kulav damo 'i medaminan lah*)!" How can you prohibit the student from drawing analogies from his teacher's rulings when "the entire Torah" – all our legal learning – is based upon that process of reasoning? To resolve this difficulty, the Talmud quotes Rav Ashi, who emends or reinterprets the *baraita* as follows: "So long as one does not draw an analogy in matters of *tereifot*," those physical injuries that disqualify kosher species of animals from consumption by Jews. In support of this emendation, the Talmud cites another tanaitic passage, which reads: "We do not draw analogies between *tereifot*. And do not be puzzled by this, for one can cut an animal on one side and it will live and on the other side and it will die." This second *baraita* (as well as the first one, under Rav Ashi's reinterpretation) instructs us not to reason analogically when learning the specific field of animal anatomy. We should not, for example, draw conclusions about injuries to an animal's liver by comparing them to similar injuries to its lung, because the physiology of each of the bodily organs is unique.[50] The objection – "so long as one does not draw an analogy" – is thus restricted to a condemnation of analogy when pursued in one particular field of law. This would lead to the inference that, in all other fields, reasoning by analogy is an appropriate method of deriving legal meaning. Various *rishonim* do make that inference. R. Meir Halevy Abulafiah (13th-century Spain) writes: "But in all other matters of Torah we do draw analogies, for not all laws, either of a monetary or ritual nature, are written explicitly. Should an issue not explicitly written present itself, we have no choice but to compare it to a similar matter discussed explicitly in the Talmud. Indeed, the rabbis of the Talmud themselves draw conclusions by analogy in their formulations of the law (*shemateta*) and in their rulings in actual cases (*uvdei*)."[51] Similarly, R. Asher b. Yechiel (Rosh, 13th–14th century Germany and Spain) declares: "We learn from case to case, by analogy, for the Sages of the Talmud were unable to provide legal guidance for every case and every new problem that would one day arise. Those that have succeeded them follow in their footsteps and use analogies therefore to learn the law."[52] As Rashi (11th-century France-Germany) notes, the very process called *talmud* consists of "the deducing of conclusions from the words of the Mishnah and the use of analogy" (*medamei milta lemilta*).[53] Consider the following example, one of many that obviously could be chosen to illustrate. In *B. Kidushin* 59a, we read that Rav Gidal was "examining" (*mehafikh*) a plot of land, that is, he was engaged in efforts to purchase it (Rashi, *s.v. mehafekh behahi ara*). Before he concluded his negotiations, Rabbi Abba came along and purchased the land. Rav Gidal filed a formal protest before the sage Rav Yitzchak bar Napacha, who confronted Rabbi Abba and asked him: "Suppose a poor man is examining a cake, and another man comes along and takes it from him. What is the rule in that case?" Rabbi Abba responded: "That other man is called 'wicked'." "Then why," asked Rav Yitzchak, "did you behave in that manner in this case?" Rabbi Abba answered: "I did not know that Rav Gidal was seeking to purchase that plot of land." Here, the poor person seeking to acquire a cake is the source case from which we learn the law concerning the target case, Rabbi Abba's purchase of land over which negotiations are taking place. Just as in the source case, so in the target case: the acquisition of the cake/land is valid, but the one who acquires it is branded as "wicked" and subject to public condemnation[54] because he acquired it while the poor person/other prospective buyer was seeking it. Although Rav Yitzchak might have used the figure of the poor person purely as a rhetorical device, the Talmud and the subsequent codifiers accept the comparison as halakhically determinative: "If one is seeking to purchase or rent an object, whether land or chattel, a second person who preempts him and acquires that object is branded as 'wicked.'"[55] Given that the rule is based on an analogy, the commentators accordingly debate the extent of the comparison. Some say that the rule applies only when the property in question is ownerless (*hefker*) or a gift, for such would likely be the case when a "poor person" is attempting to acquire a "cake." Others contend that the law covers only those cases where the second person buys the property, since that condition matches the case of Rav Gidal and Rabbi Abba. It is only because Rabbi Abba buys the property that he deserves to be called "wicked," since he could have left Rav Gidal alone and bought some other property. Such would obviously not be the case if the property was ownerless, since no such bargain probably exists elsewhere.[56] Meanwhile, early halakhists extended the analogy to matters of marital law: an agent appointed to betroth a wife for his client is called "wicked" if he betroths that woman to himself.[57] And in 1956, R. Moshe Feinstein, the preeminent *posek* (halakhic decisor) of North American Orthodox Jewry, was asked whether the rule of "the poor man examining a cake" extended to the case of *shidukhin*, a couple who were informally engaged to be married. While Feinstein answered in the negative, he did so by first examining whether the analogy to the target case *(shidukhin)* was an apt one. In any event, none of the development of this area of the law could be imagined without recourse to argument from analogy. Yet even though analogy is central to the process of talmudic and halakhic thought, both the sages and their rabbinical successors express considerable ambivalence over the use of analogy in the learning of the law. In *B. Yevamot* 109b, R. Yitzchak interprets Proverbs 11:15 to say that "evil upon evil will befall...the one who nails himself (*tokea atzmo*) to the matter of the law." The Talmud offers two explanations for this expression. According to the first, the one who "nails himself" in this manner is he who studies Torah but does not fulfill other *mitzvot*.[58] The second explanation is that the term refers to a scholar that reaches a decision in a case by relying on (*i.e., toke`a,* "nailing himself to") his own power of analogy rather than consulting a more knowledgeable scholar. This is contrasted to the dictum of R. Yonatan: "A judge should always imagine that a sword is pointed at his loins and that Hell lies open below him."[59] The judge must approach the task of halakhic decision in a spirit of the utmost seriousness, and he who decides on the basis of his own analogical reasoning without seeking the help of a more competent scholar fails in this task. Both Maimonides[60] and the *Shulchan Arukh*[61] cite this passage as authoritative *halakhah*: one must not decide a case on the basis of an analogy that one has drawn if one can consult a more knowledgeable judge ("if there is a more knowledgeable judge in the city"). R. Menachem HaMe'iri (13th–14th century Provence) expresses this idea in stronger terms:[62] "Whoever is able to clarify a matter with his teacher or a competent scholar but chooses instead to rely upon his own knowledge, drawing analogies and ruling on the basis of his own logic, deserves the curse of the sages (*kelelat chakhamim)*[63] and the severest condemnation, for he does not approach the task of halakhic decision with the proper reverence."

　　None of these talmudic and halakhic statements, of course, criticize analogical reasoning per se. Their concern is that an unqualified or mediocre scholar can easily abuse that method of thought. His decision, based upon improper analogies, may well be incorrect; moreover, his determination to rule on his own in this way is an improper arrogation of authority in the presence of his teacher[64] or of a more competent scholar. From this it would follow that there is no objection to the use of analogy (1) by a truly competent scholar, (2) by a lesser scholar when no greater authority is available for consultation, or (3) by a student who has received permission (*reshut*) from his teacher to rule on matters of *halakhah*.[65] Still, these passages, which underscore the risks inherent with analogy, hardly constitute a ringing rabbinical endorsement of that method of reasoning. Analogy in this context is contrasted unfavorably with *rules*, clear statements of the *halakhah* that one receives from a teacher or a knowledgeable scholar: we would much prefer to decide a case based upon the latter source of information than upon the former. Analogy may be the path we take when we have no other, better recourse for learning the law. But it is and remains a speculative and uncertain means of proof; as the Talmud rhetorically puts it: "Shall we issue a ruling in an actual case merely because we can draw an analogy?"[66] This, perhaps, is simply another way of saying that, just as lawyers and ethicists have never conclusively solved the "problem of importance" that attaches to every analogy, neither have the rabbis succeeded in removing the element of judgment that exists in each use of this form of reasoning. As we have seen, analogy by its nature requires a measurement of probabilities. The author of the analogy must argue that the similarities between the two objects of comparison are more important, legally and ethically speaking, than the differences between them. Such an argument will never be completely free of uncertainty, simply because analogy will always fall short of demonstrable proof. To adopt Newman's terminology, an analogy will be deemed persuasive largely to the extent that its intended audience accepted the interpretive assumptions upon which it is tacitly based, yet the validity of those assumptions may remain irremediably controversial. For this reason, the texts tell us not to rely upon analogy as a basis for halakhic decision when other, more authoritative sources of the law (books;[67] the advice of a competent scholar) are available.

III. *Analogy in Contemporary Halakhah: The Treatment of the Terminally Ill.* Analogy, therefore, is accorded a decidedly mixed reception in the Jewish legal tradition. As in law and ethics, analogy is a "necessary and ubiquitous" tool in halakhic thought. Without it, rabbis from talmudic times onward would have been unable to derive knowledge of the law in new and unprecedented matters and cases. If anything, analogy is even more important in Jewish law than in other legal traditions. Given the absence of a universally recognized legislative authority empowered to create new law, halakhists have utilized "judicial" tools, interpretation of texts and analogical reasoning from previous cases, as their (almost) exclusive mechanism for deriving legal guidance for new situations. At the same time, like their counterparts in other legal and ethical traditions, the rabbis recognize the uncertainties inherent in the analogical method, which as we have seen inevitably involves the element of judgment and the reliance upon indemonstrable interpretive assumptions to solve the "problem of importance."

All this leads to my reexamination of the issue that serves as the springboard for Louis Newman's observations: the cessation of medical treatment for a terminally ill patient. As he has noted, much of the Jewish ethical discussion of this question involves analogies based upon traditional texts that, to put it mildly, do not mention respirators, heart-lung machines, feeding tubes, aggressive experimental surgeries, and any of the other sophisticated technologies that can maintain a patient's vital signs or extend her life for a brief or extended span of time long after any realistic hope for curing or containing her disease has vanished. There exists, in other words, a "technological gap" between the traditional texts (source or basepoint cases) and the contemporary medical situation (the target or problem case) that questions the cogency of any analogy drawn from the latter to the former. My reexamination therefore will focus upon whether halakhic writers display an awareness of this gap and whether and to what extent they succeed in bridging it. I want to confine this study to specifically *halakhic* as opposed to ethical writings. As I have noted, there is considerable overlap between these subject areas in Jewish thought. Most Jewish writing on "ethical" subjects draws heavily upon halakhic sources, for the simple reason that *halakhah* is the genre of Jewish literature in which questions of praxis, ethical as well as ritual, tend to be most thoroughly analyzed, elaborated, and argued. The difference between the two may lie more in the realm of identification than of essence: by "halakhic" writings, I mean literature produced by scholars who work self-consciously within the framework of Jewish law, who see themselves as "halakhists" addressing a community of readers with a similar interest, rather than as "ethicists." By *halakhah,* moreover, I mean Jewish legal thought of the liberal as well as the traditional variety; hence, I will survey five such statements produced by Orthodox writers as well as the Central Conference of American Rabbis Responsa Committee's 1994 *teshuvah* "The Treatment of the Terminally Ill." I choose this halakhic focus– both because of my own interest in halakhic literature and because Newman largely ignores this genre in his article.[68] Analogical reasoning, in addition, figures prominently in these halakhic writings, and this will afford us sufficient data with which to consider how (and how well) analogy functions within both Orthodox and progressive halakhic discussion of this critical issue of medical ethics.

I want specifically to explore two questions, the first procedural and the second somewhat more substantive. The procedural question is one that I have already indicated: I want to know whether those who make these analogies display an awareness of the technological gap and, if so, do they inform us of the "interpretive assumptions" that enable them to overcome that gap and use the traditional texts as analogical sources for bioethical guidance. That is, I want to know how well halakhic writers succeed in meeting the challenge that Newman poses to Jewish bioethicists. The substantive question asks whether these analogies *work:* Do the authors who use them make a plausible case on behalf of their argument? Do they solve, or at least come close to solving, the "problem of importance" that attaches to analogies in general and to the "woodchopper" analogy in particular? Or, as the liberal critics charge, is the gap between the source and the target cases so wide as to render the analogies irremediably forced and artificial? The substantive question, of course, requires an evaluative judgment, which means that it lies beyond the realm of objectivity and is not subject to demonstrable proof. Still, we have no choice but to attempt evaluation simply because analogy is so vital to halakhic and ethical thinking. If the analogies *work,* then halakhists and Jewish bioethicists can claim a degree of success for their approach to the material. Conversely, to the extent that analogical thinking cannot overcome the gaps, technological or otherwise, between the traditional sources of Jewish law and the bioethical questions we face today, it will become correspondingly harder to defend "Jewish bioethics," of either the Orthodox or the Progressive variety, as a coherent discipline that has much of a future.

We begin with a consideration of three texts that have tended to serve as the basepoint or source cases for these analogies. The first of these is *Shulchan Arukh Yoreh Deah* 339:1:[69]

> The *goses* is like a living person in all legal respects. It is forbidden to bind his cheeks, or to anoint him or to cleanse his body or stop up his orifices. It is forbidden to remove the mattress from beneath him or to place him upon sand, clay, or earth. It is forbidden to place vessels of water or a grain of salt upon his abdomen. It is forbidden to announce his death or to hire musicians or wailers for his funeral. It is forbidden to close his eyelids until his soul has departed. Indeed, whoever closes the eyelids of the *goses* as his soul is departing is a shedder of blood....

From here we learn that the dying person is still alive and therefore must not be treated as though he is dead. Some of these forbidden acts describe measures taken to prepare a corpse for burial.[70] Others relate directly to our issue: to touch a *goses,* to move his body, or even to close his eyelids at the moment of death is tantamount to an act of murder. The tanaitic sources for this rule cite the following analogy:[71] the *goses* is like a dripping candle, which will extinguish at the slightest touch. "Likewise, one who closes the eyelids of the *goses* is considered as having released his soul [i.e., killed him]."[72]

Rabbi Moshe Isserles pursues the theme in his gloss to this passage:[73] Similarly, it is forbidden to hasten the death of the dying person. For example, in the case of one who has been a *goses* for an extended period of time and is unable to die [literally, "whose soul is unable to separate from his body"], it is forbidden to move the pillows and mattress from beneath him, which is done because some people believe that the feathers of certain birds hinder the person's death. Likewise, it is forbidden to move him from his place or to place the keys of the synagogue underneath his head in order that his soul might depart.

On the other hand, he continues:

> If there is present any factor which prevents the soul from departing, such as the sound of a woodcutter near the house or salt on the patient's tongue...it is permitted to remove that factor. This is not considered an act of commission (*maaseh*) but merely the removal of an impediment.

Herein, according to the Jewish ethicists whom Newman critiques, lies a major Jewish textual warrant both for the distinction between killing the terminally ill patient and letting that person die as well as for the permit to withdraw or discontinue life-sustaining therapies regarded as medically futile. The respirator is analogized to the woodchopper and to the salt: if the latter may be removed, so, too, may we disconnect the former.

The second text is the narrative in *B. Ketubot* 104a concerning the death of Rabbi Yehudah HaNasi ("Rabbi," Judah the Prince). Rabbi's students have gathered at their dying teacher's bedside to pray for his life. Their prayers have the effect of keeping him alive, but they cannot bring about his recovery. Rabbi's maidservant climbs to the attic and adds her prayer to theirs, but when she sees that Rabbi is suffering great pain, she prays for his death. When the students do not cease their own prayers, she drops a glass vessel from the attic to the floor. The students, startled by the crashing sound, cease their prayers for an instant, and in that instant Rabbi dies. The ethicists draw an *analogy* from the students' prayer to modern medical technologies that are successful in keeping terminal patients alive even as they offer no hope for recovery. If we are entitled to interrupt the prayers, the reasoning goes, we are similarly permitted to turn off the machines and to discontinue the futile treatment.

The third text (*B. Avodah Zarah* 18a) is the story of the martyr's death of R. Chaninah b. Teradyon during the Hadrianic persecutions of the second century C. E. The Romans tied R. Chaninah to a stake, wrapped him in a Torah scroll, and set him ablaze. In addition, they placed wet woolen sponges on his body to retard the flames in order that he die more slowly and painfully. R. Chaninah's students implored their teacher to open his mouth, swallow the flames, and thus die more quickly. He responded: "Let the One who gave me life take it away; one should not bring physical harm to oneself."[74] Eventually, a Roman officer at the scene offers to remove the wet sponges and to increase the intensity of the fire in return for R. Chaninah's assurance that the officer might receive life in the World to Come. R. Chaninah accepts the offer; and "his soul departed quickly." A heavenly voice thereupon affirms the righteousness of both men when it declares: "R. Chaninah b. Teradyon and the officer are destined for life in the World to Come." Some obvious problems are associated with learning bioethics from a narrative concerning a martyr's death. And a glaring contradiction is to be resolved: Whereas removing the wet sponges could conceivably be defined as the removal of an impediment to death, to increase the intensity of the fire seems more akin to an active measure designed to hasten death. Still, provided that these difficulties can be successfully addressed,[75] the story might serve as an analogy or precedent for the removal of life support and other therapies when these are judged to be medically futile.

1. *R. Immanuel Jakobovits.* One of the early pioneers of the discipline that came to be known as Jewish bioethics,[76] R. Immanuel Jakobovits discusses the treatment of the terminally ill in a 1956 article that appeared in an Orthodox halakhic journal.[77] Then chief rabbi of Ireland, future chief rabbi of the United Kingdom, and a preeminent figure in the discipline that came to be known as Jewish bioethics, having previously established that Jewish law forbids any positive action undertaken to shorten human life,[78] Jakobovits declares that "the rules are entirely different" when it comes to taking no action to extend the life of the *goses* or to remove an impediment to his death. Basing his analysis upon all three of our "basepoint" texts, he adds an important element to the discussion of Isserles's permit to remove an impediment to death. The commentators to the *Shulchan Arukh* notice an apparent contradiction among the list of examples that Isserles cites. It is forbidden to remove the pillows and mattress from beneath the *goses,* even though this action could be defined as the removal of an impediment to death (the feathers), because it necessarily involves the physical movement of the *goses.* If so, why is it permitted to remove the salt from his tongue? Doesn't that also require physical contact and the movement of his body?[79] An answer is anticipated in *Shiltey Giborim,* a 16th-century commentary to the *Halakhot* of Alfasi:[80] just as it is forbidden to hasten the death of the dying person, it is also forbidden to introduce a factor into his situation – such as placing salt on his tongue – that would unnecessarily delay his otherwise inevitable and imminent death. For this reason, it is permitted to remove that factor from the scene, even if the removal involves a minimal amount of contact with the patient's body.[81] "From this," writes Jakobovits, "we learn that not only is it permitted to remove an impediment to death but also that it is forbidden to hinder unnecessarily the departure of the soul and thus extend the suffering of the patient *(hacholeh).*"

Although Jakobovits, speaking of the removal of "impediments to death," has suggested the medical implications of these texts, he has to claim explicitly that they bear such meaning. It is therefore at this point that he makes a crucial methodological observation:

> Admittedly, (in this question) we are not concerned with non-natural factors. At any rate, it would seem that as a matter of principle the spirit of the Torah is not utterly indifferent *(ein ruach hatorah mitnaker legamrei)* to the plea of the suffering to be released from their affliction. From that standpoint, these texts are very important to us, especially because they emphasize once again the significant difference between taking active measures to shorten life and removing that which is merely an impediment to death.

This, of course, is a powerfully rhetorical passage. What good Jew would imagine that "the spirit of the Torah" is so callous as to ignore human suffering? Yet the rhetoric is hardly a superfluous effort; it cannot be dismissed as a mere literary flourish. Jakobovits, like every author of an essay in persuasive communication, wants his intended audience to accept his claim of meaning upon the data (in this case, the canonical Jewish texts). He therefore bases his claim in a statement of what he perceives as a value commitment to which his audience will certainly assent, namely the belief in the Torah's compassion for the dying. That statement, in turn, formulates the interpretive assumption through which Jakobovits validates his analogies. He recognizes clearly the technological gap between "non-natural factors" (prayer, the woodchopper, the salt, the keys to the synagogue, etc.) and the world of modern biotechnology. The analogy from the former to the latter is therefore a problematic one. Nonetheless, our commitment to relieve human suffering, rooted in and validated by the "spirit of the Torah," allows us to read – and, indeed, demands that we read – the traditional texts as legitimate basepoint cases from which to derive guidance concerning contemporary medical dilemmas. By making his assumption clear, Jakobovits responds to one of the two principal criticisms that Newman raises against some Jewish bioethicists who have addressed our topic.

With respect to Newman's second critique, Jakobovits is also clear. He acknowledges the limits of the analogy, that the ruling of Isserles applies only to a patient who is already a *goses*. A different theoretical approach is required to justify the discontinuation of medical treatment for a *choleh noash*, a patient who, though not yet in the very last stages of life, has been diagnosed as terminal with no hope of recovery. Jakobovits offers that rationale in the form of a *chidush,* an idea of his own derivation that he uses to resolve a conflict between Nachmanides and Maimonides concerning the toraitic source of the *mitzvah* to practice medicine. Whereas the intricacies of that *chidush* do not concern us here,[82] Jakobovits uses it to distinguish between permitted and obligatory medical treatment. While a terminal patient is *permitted* to undertake medical measures "that keep him alive in a state of suffering," he is not *obligated* to do so. One practical conclusion of this distinction, writes Jakobovits, applies to the instance of a diabetic who develops terminal cancer. The insulin injections that she takes for her diabetes and that heretofore have been regarded as part of a successful regimen of treatment can be said now to function so as to extend her agony. Though she is permitted to continue with those injections, "one should not object" should she decide to cease them. In his essay, then, Jakobovits makes extensive though not unlimited use of the analogies that figure prominently in Jewish bioethical discussions of the treatment of the terminally ill. He addresses "the problem of importance" by arguing forcefully that the similarities between the baseline cases and the target case outweigh the differences between them. He also recognizes that the analogies have their limits and should not be extended farther than they can plausibly take us.

2. *Rabbi Barukh Rabinovitz.* Writing in 1979 in the medical-halakhic journal *Asya*,[83] Barukh Rabinovitz addresses the ruling by Isserles (i.e., the woodchopper, the salt, etc.) as follows:

> This *halakhah* is quite significant in considering the workings of modern medicine. In their efforts to save a patient's life (the doctors) will attach him to all sorts of machines (*kol miney mekhonot*) that deliver oxygen and medications to all parts of his body. As long as the body is connected to these devices, it can remain alive in what the physicians call "a vegetative state" for a very long time…. The question: is it permissible to disconnect these devices so long as the patient's vital signs continue to function? The physician has indeed given up all hope of restoring the patient to normal (*tiviim*) and spontaneous life, but the patient can continue to exist in this state of artificial life *(chayim malakhutiim)*. Is the physician permitted to bring an end to that life? This is a problem that we encounter in hospitals almost every day. Many physicians ask what they are supposed to do, for the patient will die at the moment they disconnect the device. Is this not to be defined as causing death by active means...?

> This *halakhah*, which distinguishes between shortening the life of the *goses* and the removal of an impediment to the departure of his soul – **that is, the artificial extension of the life of the goses** [my emphasis –. MW] supplies a clear answer to this question. The machine operates for all practical purposes to delay artificially the departure of the soul…. It is obligatory, therefore, to disconnect the patient from the machine and to allow nature to take its course until he dies.

Rhetoric is present here as well. The phrase "all sorts of machines" expresses something of the bewilderment and frustration of the layperson at the vast array of modern technological marvels that, at the end of the day, offer not healing but extended suffering and medical futility. The vegetative state is emblematic of that futility: Who would regard such an outcome as successful treatment, and who would want it for herself or her loved ones? The doctors, for their part, are described as being at wit's end as to how to care for patients who are so obviously beyond all medical help. The repeated use of the word "artificial" *(malakhuti/malakhutiim)* in counterpoint to the reference to "normal" (or "natural"; *tiviim*) also emphasizes the situation of futility: "artificial life" strikes the reader as no life at all, a state of existence we would wish to end as quickly as possible.

Rabinovitz thus invites his readers to join him in a quest for a practical and compassionate solution that, presumably, they desire as much as he does. In addition, the notion of "artificial life" serves as Rabinovitz's interpretive assumption: the nonmedical impediments of which Isserles speaks share with modern biomedical technology the capacity to extend life *artificially,* in a condition not contemplated in the natural or divinely-intended order of things. The artificiality that defines both the woodchopper and the respirator is the significant link between them, and in this way Rabinovitz claims to solve the "problem of importance" that plagues every analogy.

3. *Dr. Ya`akov Levy.* A physician and Torah scholar, Ya'akov Levy addresses our subject in an essay appearing in the 1973 edition of *Noam*, a halakhic annual published by the Chief Rabbinate of Israel. In direct response to the words of Rabinovitz cited above, he writes: [84]

> As a physician, I perceive substantial biological distinctions between the situation that Isserles describes and that of the heart-lung machine, with respect to both the patient's condition and to the physician's role.... The patient of whom Isserles speaks rests with certainty at the last moment before death. The patient who is connected to the machine, by contrast, is in an uncertain situation. The physicians cannot

declare with absolute confidence that he is dead or even that he
is going to die. It may yet be possible to save his life, for it was
for that purpose that he was connected in the first place to the
machine.

Another difference: there are substantial biological differences
between the actions taken in the two cases. The machine serves
a vital medical function, supplying oxygen, nutrition, and
hydration to every part of the body. To turn off the machine
would prevent these vital substances from reaching the body.
Such is not the case with removing the sound of the
woodchopper or the grains of salt from upon the tongue. It is
difficult to define the interruption of the flow of oxygen as, to
use the terminology of Isserles, "not an act of commission."

Unlike Jakobovits and Rabinovitz, Levy rejects the relevance
of the woodchopper analogy, for reasons that parallel both aspects of
Newman's critique of the bioethicists. The patient of whom Isserles
speaks is a *goses,* a state in which the imminence of death is a
certainty. Yet *our* patient, precisely because she is connected to
machines that perform vital medical and biological life-support
functions, *cannot* be described as a *goseset.* Levy's guiding
interpretive assumption is a negative one: it is improper to
compare modern medical technology (particularly the heart-lung
machine) to the supernatural elements described in the *Shulchan
Arukh*. The analogy fails, therefore, because the differences between
the target and the baseline cases as substantially more significant than
their similarities. Here, too, we detect the author's use of rhetoric as a
means of supporting his interpretive assumption. Levy introduces his
comments here and elsewhere[85] by reminding the reader that he is a
physician and that he speaks from a basis of medical knowledge that,
by definition, lies beyond the expertise of some rabbis who write about
the subject. He presents his *bona fides* as a scientist as a reason why
his readers should reject the attempts of other Torah scholars to make
the woodchopper analogy: It is as a *doctor* that he declares the source

and target cases more dissimilar than similar. The opposing point of view, which accepts the analogy as cogent, must consequently rest upon a basis of medical ignorance or naiveté. The appeal here, in classical rhetorical terms, is to *ethos*, the speaker's reliability on the subject as evidence on behalf of his argument.[86]

4. *R. Eliezer Yehudah Waldenberg.* The author of the multivolume series of responsa entitled *Tzitz Eliezer,* Rabbi Eliezer Yehudah Waldenberg, is a widely recognized authority on matters of medical *halakhah*.[87] In a reply to a 1976 inquiry by Dr. David Meir, the administrator of Shaare Zedek Medical Center in Jerusalem, Waldenberg wrote a lengthy responsum in support of Meir's suggestion that patients who display no signs of "independent vitality" *(chayim atzmi'im or chayut atzmit)* be disconnected from the artificial respirator that maintains their breathing.[88] In Meir's description, this category of cases includes patients brought to the emergency room following a major trauma, often a serious traffic accident that has left them with crushed skulls. In the effort to stabilize their vital signs and determine whether their lives can be saved, the patients are immediately placed on respirators. These machines function entirely "from the outside," pumping oxygen into the lungs, and they can continue to do so almost indefinitely even after the patient has lost all ability to breathe on his own. Only later during the treatment does it become apparent that the patient has no "independent vitality" – "the brain has no control over the inflation of the lung" – and has thus lost any chance for recovery. Meir mentions the ruling of Isserles in *Shulchan Arukh Yoreh Deah* 339. May we compare the two cases? Are we entitled at this point to define the respirator as an "impediment," a factor that does nothing but prevent the otherwise imminent death of the patient, and thus to disconnect it?

Waldenberg accepts the analogy. He focuses particularly on the conclusion, which some authorities have derived from the Isserles text, that just as it is forbidden to take an active step to hasten death, so is it forbidden to introduce a factor that will unnecessarily delay death.[89] He asks why this is so, given that Jewish law generally teaches that it is a *mitzvah* to preserve life, even *chayei shaah,* the brief amount of life that remains for a dying person? Why then are we forbidden to introduce "impediments" into the situation? Why, indeed, are we not obligated to *delay* the death of the dying person for as long as possible? He locates the answer to this question in the common denominator running through Isserles's examples (the woodchopper, the salt, the feathers), namely, their externality. That is, it is forbidden to introduce these measures precisely because they do not contribute anything to the independent vitality *(chayut atzmit)* of the *goses*, his ability to maintain life on his own. Any factor that simply maintains the vital signs from outside the patient's body but does not contribute to his recovery of independent vitality is by definition an impediment to death that should not be introduced *ab initio* and that, if introduced, may (and perhaps must) be removed.[90]

> We do not conclude that this would be considered an act to hasten death, for such is contrary to the will of God. Indeed, the sort of life that he has now is entirely the product of human artifice, and we learn that to extend such a life is contrary to the will of God from *Sefer Chasidim,* chapter 234: "We do not cry out at the moment of the soul's departure, lest it return and the person suffer terrible agony. Why did Kohelet write that 'there is a time to die' (Eccl. 3:2) if not to tell us that the *goses* should not be forced to endure another day or two of needless suffering?".... Thus we learn that we should undertake no act to resuscitate the patient when it is clear to us that it is his "time to die."... This is contrary to the will of God, who has declared that "man exercises no control over the day of his death,"[91] and it is not within human authority to continue to live in this state when it is obvious that "the time to die" has arrived.

Waldenberg therefore applies the woodchopper analogy to the contemporary medical scene. He does so, even though the respirator is quite different technologically from the supernatural factors that Isserles mentions because it resembles them in terms of function: like the woodchopper and the salt, the respirator at this moment is an entirely external force, pushing life into the patient from the outside but unable to help him recover the power to live on his own.[92] His "interpretive assumption"– the general theoretical approach that justifies the analogy and that determines the similarities in the cases to be more important than their differences – is that God has decreed that the *goses* has reached the "time to die" and that God does not wish him to continue life under these circumstances. Waldenberg's repeated reference to "the will of God" is therefore a theological claim on behalf of his interpretive assumption. His rhetoric appeals to his religious reader's presumed agreement that not everything in the world is subject to human control and that some medical measures, though materially within our power, lie beyond the sphere of legitimate human authority.

5. *R. Moshe Feinstein.* Responding in 1982 to a series of questions on medical ethics submitted by two physicians, Rabbi Moshe Feinstein takes up the following issue: Is it permissible to refrain from administering life-extending treatment to some patients?[93] He begins by reciting the story of the death of R. Yehudah HaNasi (*B. Ketubot* 104a). "The Talmud tells this story," he writes, "in order to teach that there are times, when a person is suffering and when neither medicine nor prayer suffices to restore him to health, that one must pray for his death, as did Rabbi's maidservant." Feinstein notes that he derives this conclusion from the 14th century R. Nissim Gerondi, who makes the point in his commentary to *B. Nedarim* 40a. Feinstein thereupon makes the analogy to the contemporary medical situation: In the absence of a medical remedy that will enable the patient to survive his illness *(efshar lo sheyichyeh)* and when the patient is suffering terrible pain *(yisurin),* physicians should not provide treatment that can do

nothing but extend the patient's life in its present state. In saying this, Feinstein is careful to affirm the traditional Jewish teachings concerning the value of even the shortest span of human life. Thus, only "passive" actions (the removal of an impediment) are permitted, "since to initiate any action that will shorten life by even a moment is considered bloodshed." A near-death patient must be given oxygen, "because to do so will ease his suffering." When the oxygen in the tank runs out, however, the physicians may examine the patient to see whether he has died. "In this way, there is no concern that the doctors will kill the patient… even by depriving him of the briefest moment of life *(cahyei sha'ah haketzarah beyoter)*."

Feinstein's ruling stirred some further questions, to which he addressed himself two years later in a *teshuvah* to R. Sholom Tendler.[94] In this second missive he restates his opinion that doctors should not administer therapy that cannot offer recovery to the terminal patient and that promises only to extend his life in its present condition of suffering. He once again cites *B. Ketubot* 104a, along with R. Nissim's commentary, but this time he emphasizes not the maidservant's prayer but the action she took to interrupt the prayers of Rabbi's students. This marks a significant shift from his earlier *teshuvah,* in which he stressed the lesson that just as the maidservant prayed for Rabbi to die, "there are times when we must pray for the death" of the terminal patient. Feinstein now rejects the analogy from the maidservant's prayer to our own: "our prayers today are not so readily accepted, so we should not learn from the ineffectiveness of our prayers for the patient's recovery that it is permissible to pray for his death, God forbid." The analogy that *does* work, however, is the analogy of the maidservant's interruption of the prayers and the withholding or withdrawal of medical treatment that merely extends pain and suffering but offers no hope for recovery. Yet while Feinstein reasserts his support for the discontinuation of futile treatments, he introduces here two limitations on his otherwise permissive ruling. First, he declares that the patient must be kept alive, even in his suffering, if there is a chance that another, more knowledgeable physician can in the meantime be consulted about the case. Second, he emphasizes that his permit applies only to situations where the patient is experiencing *yisurin*, physical suffering.

> It is obvious *(pashut)* that R. Moshe Isserles would agree. Although in *Yoreh Deah* 339 he permits the removal of a factor that impedes the departure of the soul, it is obvious *(pashut)* that he does so solely because of the *yisurin* that the *goses* experiences. In the absence of pain, there is no reason to permit even the removal of a factor that impedes the departure of the soul. On the contrary, we would be obligated to introduce such a factor into the situation.... Why would we endeavor to remove impediments to death if the patient were not in pain? Rather, it is certain *(vadai)* that the permit to remove impediments is because the *goses* suffers pain when his death is an extended process. It is certain *(vadai)* that R. Moshe Isserles and those who preceded him possessed an authoritative tradition on this point.

Here Feinstein states the interpretive assumption that governs his use of the analogy. Despite the technological gap that separates the target case (the contemporary question of withholding medical treatment from the terminally ill) and the basepoint cases (*B. Ketubot* 104a and, to a lesser extent, Isserles in *Yoreh Deah* 339), the two are significantly similar in their concern that we not prolong the suffering of a dying person when there is no medical remedy for him. Yet even as he draws the analogy, Feinstein sharply restricts its scope. The warrant to discontinue or withhold treatment exists only in cases where two factors are present: the patient has no hope for recovery and is suffering great pain. This would exclude the comatose patient and the one lying in a persistent vegetative state, let alone the person who is terminally ill but not yet experiencing *yisurin*. Feinstein supports this limitation not by citing texts but by claiming that the limitation is "obvious" or "certain." This may weaken his argument to some extent, since assertion is hardly the same as demonstrated proof. Still, an assertion can be quite effective when its intended audience regards it as axiomatic, as a self-evident starting point for argument. By calling the limitation "obvious," Feinstein invokes as his audience precisely that community of readers who will in fact regard it as obvious, namely those Orthodox Jews who share his belief in the sanctity of even the shortest span of human life *(chayei shaah)* and the concomitant requirement that medicine do everything possible to preserve life to its very last instant.[95] This audience would presumably accept Feinstein's claim that intolerable physical suffering constitutes an exception to the rule; after all, the story of Rabbi's maidservant seems explicit on that point, and Feinstein thinks it "obvious" or "certain" that pain is the dominant factor in the Isserles text as well.[96] At the same time, the audience would probably oppose any effort to extend the range of this exception to other sets of circumstances, and Feinstein, accordingly, makes clear in this second *teshuvah* that no warrant other than severe pain suffices to justify the discontinuation of medical treatment for a terminal patient.[97] Taken together, these shared beliefs – that every moment of human life is sacred and that we have a moral obligation to spare the dying needless suffering – constitute the interpretive assumption that on the one hand allows him to read the texts as supporting the discontinuation of medical treatment while on the other hand limiting that warrant to cases in which the *goses* is suffering physical pain and agony.

6. Central Conference of American Rabbis *Responsum no. 5754.11.* In 1994 the Responsa Committee of the issued its *teshuvah* "On the Treatment of the Terminally Ill."[98] The responsum addresses the "woodchopper" analogy in section II, "The Cessation of Medical Treatment for Terminal Patients," citing the Isserles passage along with the extensive commentary it has received, as "the classic source" for the halakhic discussion of the issue. The Committee notes that despite the obvious differences between Isserles's "impediments" and

the world of modern medicine, various halakhic authorities have adopted the analogy and argued for its relevance.

> This theory[99] helps to translate the medieval language of the texts into a usable contemporary vernacular. Does there not come a point in a patient's condition when, despite their obvious life-saving powers, the sophisticated technologies of modern medicine – the mechanical respirator, for example, or the heart-lung machine–become nothing more than mere "salt on the tongue," mechanisms which maintain the patient's vital signs long after all hope of recovery has vanished? Answering "yes" to this question, some contemporary *poskim*[100] allow the respirator to be disconnected when a patient is clearly and irrevocably unable to sustain independent heartbeat and respiration.

Here the responsum identifies and clarifies the interpretive assumption by means of which halakhists can usefully analogize from the Isserles text to contemporary medical technology: when treatment can do nothing more than keep the "vital signs" going in the absence of any hope for recovery, they become the functional equivalent of the woodchopper and salt on the tongue. This assumption is stated in the form of a rhetorical question that suggests that the responsum's authors expect their readers to accept its cogency. The text goes on to say, however, that not all halakhic writers accept the analogy, since woodchoppers and bird feathers and salt can be described as "scientific" or "technological" only with great difficulty. Moreover, even if we did draw the analogy from medieval "science" to that of our own day, the classical source speaks only of the *goses*, whose death is imminent; it tells us little or nothing about the terminally ill patient for whom the physicians see no hope for recovery but whose death may be weeks or months away. The responsum presumes, in other words, that "we" (the audience it addresses) agree that the respirator *can* be compared to the woodchopper, but it also posits that "we" would not want to stretch that analogy beyond its reasonable breaking point.

For these reasons the responsum develops, in section III, "another conceptual framework for thinking about the terminally ill patient whose death is not yet imminent." This framework is the commandment *(mitzvah)* to heal the sick. The argument, reminiscent of if not identical to the theory presented by R. Immanuel Jakobovits,[101] is that like the more general duty to save life, the *mitzvah* of medicine is obligatory only as long as it promises a reasonable chance of success.[102] Treatments that do not effect "healing" are not, therefore, regarded as "true medicine" *(refuah vadait or bedukah)*[103] and are not obligatory. Under this logic, a person who is terminally ill may refuse treatment that may extend her life expectancy a short time but that holds no prospect of curing or controlling her illness. The predominant consideration here is not necessarily that the patient will experience prolonged or greater suffering by accepting the treatment, although such might be the case, but rather that the treatment is medically futile.

The Responsa Committee acknowledges the difficulty in defining the term "medical futility"; "[i]n many situations it will be problematic if not impossible to determine when or even if the prescribed regime of therapy has lost its medical value." In the face of this systemic uncertainty, the text suggests, some may prefer to take refuge in the traditional Jewish doctrine of the sanctity of every moment of human life, which may lead them to the conclusion that one is never permitted to refuse medical treatment but is rather obligated to fight disease and cling to life until its very last instant. The Committee responds to this objection in the following manner:

> To this argument we would simply ask: is this truly "medicine" as we conceive it? Our answer, as liberal Jews who seek guidance from our tradition in facing the moral dilemmas of our age, is "no."... [W]e cannot and do not believe that

those texts, which bid us to heal the sick and to preserve life, demand that in fulfilling these duties we apply in indiscriminate fashion every available technological device to prolong the death of a dying person. Medical science has made immeasurable advances during recent times, and we are thankful for that fact. Doctors today are able to prevent and to cure disease, to offer hope to the sick and disabled to an extent that past generations could scarcely imagine. Yet there comes a point in time when all the technologies, the chemicals, the surgeries, and the machines which comprise the lifesaving arsenal of modern medicine become counterproductive, a point when all that medical science can effectively do for a patient is to indefinitely delay his inevitable death. This is not *pikuach nefesh*; this is not medicine; this is not what physicians, as agents of healing, are supposed to do. There is neither meaning nor purpose in maintaining these treatments. **They are salt on the tongue and the sound of a woodchopper** [emphasis added–MW]. They are not *refu'ah* [medicine; healing]; no commandments are fulfilled thereby. Yes, life is a precious thing, and every moment of it should be regarded as God's gift. But we are not required under any reading of the tradition that makes sense to us to buy additional moments of life undertaking useless and pointless medical treatment.

This rhetorically charged passage serves much the same purpose as R. Moshe Feinstein's use of the terms "obvious" and "certain" in his argument. The Reform responsum, no less than the Orthodox *posek,* wishes to invoke a community of interpretation, to identify the readers who are most likely to find its words persuasive and compelling. Where Feinstein's community consisted of those who hold the sanctity of even the shortest span of life to be of the ultimate value, the community envisioned by this responsum comprises those "who cannot and do not believe" that Torah demands that we undertake every conceivable technological measure to delay the otherwise inevitable death of a terminally ill   patient. As with Feinstein, this invocation of an audience has less to do with proof and evidence than with assertion: if these words resonate with you, the responsum seems to be saying, then you are the audience to whom they are addressed. Notice that the rhetoric of this passage enables the responsum's authors to rehabilitate the woodchopper analogy, which it had set aside because of its apparent weaknesses (it does not cohere with modern technology and it does not apply precisely to the case of the terminally ill patient who is not yet a *goses*). Now that the theme of therapeutic futility has become the dominant organizing principle of the *teshuvah,* the Responsa Committee is in a position to claim that medical measures that are useless in the face of terminal illness are tantamount to "salt on the tongue and the sound of a woodchopper." The Isserles text, although it speaks literally to the situation of the *goses,* is now understood to refer to any and all measures that serve to delay death while offering no medical benefit. This passage calls upon its readers to assent to the logic of the analogy, and the rhetorical question with which it commences suggests a confidence that they will do so.

IV. *Conclusions.* What has the foregoing analysis revealed about the use of analogy in the halakhic discussions concerning the treatment of the terminally ill? Let me set forth some tentative conclusions in accordance with the two questions I posed at the outset of our study.

1. Our first question was the procedural one: do these halakhic writers make clear the interpretive assumptions that enable them to use the traditional sources for purpose of analogy? We have seen that each of these authors does mention the well-known analogy between the woodchopper (or the prayer of Rabbi's maidservant, or the death of R. Chaninah b. Teradyon) and the life-sustaining technologies of modern medicine and that all , with the exception of Dr.Ya'akov Levy, do so positively. Yet we have also seen that none of them regard the analogy as self-evident and problem-free. Each one recognizes the "technological gap" that separates the source cases (the talmudic

and halakhic passages that they wish to use as precedents) and the target case (today's medical treatment of the terminally ill). Each acknowledges that the texts must be interpreted or, as the CCAR Responsa Committee puts it, "translated" into a vernacular that can speak to the contemporary medical context. Each author that accepts the analogy therefore offers reasons for *why* he accepts it, why it is proper and fitting. They are at the same time keenly aware of the analogy's limitations and take care to distinguish the cases to which it applies (the *goses*) from those to which it does not (the terminally ill patient who is not yet a *goses* or is not suffering severe pain). The exception here is the CCAR responsum, which both admits the limitation of the analogy and subsequently (following its development of an alternative theory to permit the discontinuation of futile treatment) reinterprets it so that the woodchopper and the salt function as symbolic expressions of medical futility. These writers, in other words, are cognizant that the woodchopper analogy can work only when accompanied by or filtered through what Louis Newman calls an interpretive assumption that renders it coherent and meaningful. Nothing is hidden about these assumptions. Their presence is obvious in each of these writings, and the reader can identify them with relative ease.

This last point deserves a closer look. Newman poses his challenge to Jewish bioethicists as follows: "To defend cogently any particular ethical position... requires that one offer reasons for adopting the interpretive stance that one has.... And if one wishes to urge others to adopt a particular interpretation, that theory must be stated explicitly and defended."[104] That is to say, those engaging in Jewish bioethical discourse must pass a two-stage test: they should both clearly *articulate* the interpretive assumptions that make their analogies possible and *justify* those theoretical frameworks against other possible interpretations. Our halakhic authors would clearly seem to meet the first part of this test because they do indicate for us the theoretical frameworks that justify their acceptance or rejection of the woodchopper analogy. To recap, these include: Jakobovits's remark that "as a matter of principle the spirit of the Torah is not utterly indifferent to the plea of the suffering;" Rabinovitz's invocation of "artificiality" as the common denominator between the woodchopper and the respirator; Levy's citation of his own medical expertise to justify his rejection of the woodchopper analogy; Waldenberg's conclusion that "to extend such a life [i.e., of the patient who has lost the capacity for "independent vitality"] is contrary to the will of God"; Feinstein's declaration that "it is obvious" that the impediments to the death of a *goses* may be removed precisely but only because she is suffering great pain; and the CCAR Responsa Committee's rhetorical questions ("Does there not come a point in a patient's condition when, despite their obvious life-saving powers, the sophisticated technologies of modern medicine… become nothing more than mere 'salt on the tongue'…? "To this argument we would simply ask: is this truly 'medicine' as we conceive it?"). On the other hand, not all our halakhic authors fare as well with Newman's second requirement. In particular, Rabbis Waldenberg and Feinstein are satisfied to state their own interpretive positions and do not explicitly "defend" those views and assumptions against alternative understandings of the texts. Newman, perhaps, would see this as a weakness in the halakhic discourse on this issue, similar to the one he finds in Jewish bioethical writing. We should keep in mind, however, the influence of legal genre upon these writings. Waldenberg and Feinstein write here not as bioethicists or as academic legal scholars but as *poskim*, decisors handing down definitive rulings. Their function is akin to that of judges, and judges, too, are often silent as to alternative interpretive possibilities. The judicial opinion, it has been noted, is often characterized by the "rhetoric of inevitability," in which the judge assumes a "monologic voice" or a "declarative tone" as a means of persuading the reader that he could not reasonably have come to a different conclusion. The judge may see this, in fact, as a requirement of the judicial role and hence of the opinion as a literary genre: the task of the judge, after all, is to tell us what the law is, which places a premium upon stating the law with finality and certitude.[105] By contrast, the author of a law review article reading the same legal materials the judge considers will confront other views in a much more systematic way, since that author is under no obligation to write as though only one correct answer exists. Indeed, the goal of such an article may be precisely to explore the varying possible interpretations and to raise the questions, doubts, and uncertainties the judge strives either to resolve or to ignore. Like the judge, the *posek* may not see it as his job to defend his interpretive position against all plausible alternatives, especially if in the process he suggests doubt and uncertainty as to the correctness of his own *pesak* (ruling).[106]

This suggestion – that there is a meaningful genre difference between the writing of *poskim* handing down rulings and that of halakhists engaged in a more general study of their subject – is offered here as a hypothesis; the question deserves further study. To the extent that there is something to the distinction, however, we might conclude that the primary responsibility for producing thorough and balanced analyses of alternative halakhic assumptions and positions rests not with the *poskim* but with the wider community of halakhic interpretation, just as it has been the task of scholars writing in law reviews to examine and criticize the reasoning of published judicial opinions. Such a community of halakhic "law review" scholarship does exist, especially with respect to bioethics.[107] As long as the members of that community continue to write and publish – and there is little indication that they intend to stop doing so (!) – they will ensure the continuation of a healthy discourse in the field.

2. Our second question was the substantive one: how well do these analogies work, and do they solve the "problem of importance"? As I have indicated, this question may seem difficult to address, since it demands the sort of evaluative judgment that cannot be quantified. How, after all, do we measure objectively the degree of an argument's persuasiveness? In fact, though, my question concerns not so much the persuasiveness of these analogies, the extent to which they persuade

you, or me, or some other reader(s), is their *plausibility*: Can the analogy from the woodchopper text and the other traditional passages serve as the basis of a plausible discourse concerning medical treatment for the dying? Framed in this manner, the question is much easier to answer. We can say with confidence that the woodchopper analogy *does* work and it *is* plausible, provided that the audience to which it is addressed accepts the interpretive assumptions upon which it depends. Let's take as our example Rabbi Jakobovits's analogy, based on all three of the talmudic and halakhic texts discussed at the beginning of section III. Each of these texts affirms the correctness of an action that removes an impediment to the otherwise imminent death of a *goses*. Jakobovits wishes to draw an analogy from those texts and actions to the medical treatment of the *goses*. Although conceding that the texts speak not of medical but of "non-natural" impediments to death, Jakobovits argues that they teach that "as a matter of principle the spirit of the Torah is not utterly indifferent to the plea of the suffering." On this point he bases his claim that truly medical impediments may also be removed, for even though used by physicians in fulfillment of the *mitzvah* of healing they can function at life's final stage to prolong the same sort of suffering that the Torah wishes to bring to a speedy end. Does this analogy persuade every reader? Clearly not; Dr. Ya'akov Levy, for one, doesn't accept it. Yet it is not difficult to imagine the existence of an interpretive community that *would* accept it, that would with Jakobovits find the analogy a plausible basis on which to argue that Jewish law permits the discontinuation of life-prolonging medical treatment for the terminally ill under certain circumstances. That audience would agree with Jakobovits precisely because it identifies with his interpretive assumption, the claim that "the spirit of the Torah" would have us extend compassion to those who suffer from disease and who lie near death. To adopt the assumption, in other words, is to be persuaded of the analogy's cogency. The same could be said of the writings of Rabinovitz, Waldenberg, Feinstein, and the CCAR Responsa Committee. In each case, analogies are built on interpretive assumptions that, persuasive or not, cannot readily be dismissed as implausible. I see no reason, in other words, why an audience *cannot* gather around an interpretive assumption concerning the lack of obligation to maintain "artificial" life or the claim that it is not God's will that we maintain patients in such a state, or that the suffering of the dying constitutes a reason for withdrawing medical care, that the commandment to heal does not require the indefinite continuation of measures that are medically futile. In each case, the author or authors invite their readers to identify themselves as a particular sort of Jewish audience, an audience that recognizes the interpretive assumption in question as a core value of its Judaism. To the extent that it accepts this invitation, the audience is likely to find the woodchopper analogy persuasive.

I have used the term *rhetoric,* which encompasses the techniques of persuasive speech and writing, to describe the manner in which our authors put forth this invitation to their readers. What I am describing, more specifically, is *constitutive* rhetoric, speech that does not so much persuade an already existing audience as to create (to "constitute") a new audience through its language, speech that forms the identity of the community within the message itself. In none of these cases does the interpretive assumption work to persuade the audience of its correctness. The assumption after all, is simply that: an assumption, or, if made explicit, an assertion, a claim of meaning upon the texts, but the claim does not prove itself to be true, any more than the analogy it supports can prove itself to be true. Jakobovits, for example, never demonstrates that his interpretive assumption about "the spirit of the Torah" is the correct lesson to be learned from the traditional texts; he simply asserts that lesson. Other explanations are possible, and were we to accept those explanations we might not follow Jakobovits to his conclusion about the propriety of discontinuing life-prolonging but otherwise futile medical treatment for the *goses.* Yet this lack of demonstrated proof does not doom the argument, for the interpretive assumption is the way in which Jakobovits *constitutes* the audience that will find it persuasive. By accepting his claim of meaning upon the texts, his readers answer his invitation to become his audience, identifying themselves as precisely the community to whom he addresses his words, as the community that speaks as he does about these texts and about the question of the proper medical treatment of the terminally ill. The crucial point is that his audience does not exist *prior* to his rhetorical act but *because* of it. The same would apply to the writings of the other authors we have surveyed. In each case it is the rhetoric itself, that asserts, though it does not prove, the author's interpretive assumptions, that invokes the audience he wishes to address, causing its members to become the community that understands and speaks of the bioethical issue as he does. That community, in turn, once it has been constituted by the author's words, is the community most likely to be persuaded that his analogies are fitting and correct.[108]

V. *Two Final Observations.* I have argued in this paper that the woodchopper and related analogies do support an intelligent bioethical discourse on the question of the treatment of the terminally ill. Again, this does not imply that the analogies in fact persuade all readers or that they are free of difficulty. It is to say, though, that they furnish the tools required for bioethical conversation. In other words, traditional halakhic reasoning, *characterized by its heavy reliance upon analogy,* can plausibly claim to possess the resources to analyze and respond to the challenge of this particular problem of bioethics. And this leads me, finally, to the following two observations:

The first is the simple truth that analogical reasoning, notwithstanding all its inherent difficulties, is an essential feature of halakhic discourse, just as it is an essential feature of legal and ethical discourse. One cannot operate within the field of *halakhah* and ignore this reality. There is no such thing as "Jewish legal thinking" without analogy, and Jewish legal analogies tend to be drawn from Jewish legal texts, the bulk of which are found in ancient and medieval literary sources. Those sources, by dint of their historical and cultural provenance, do not often speak explicitly to the issues raised by contemporary bioethics. They most certainly do not mention respirators and heart-lung machines. For this reason, analogies drawn from very old Jewish texts to very contemporary social and technological realities will tend to strike us as forced and artificial. Yet there is no alternative: were halakhists to abandon the method of casuistic reasoning, they would be unable to apply the classic texts of Jewish law to those realities. Therefore if we wish to do *halakhah*, if we wish to pursue the study of Torah as Jews have always done as the royal road to deriving guidance on matters of religious practice, we have no choice but to reason analogically from our traditional texts to the problems that confront us. I suppose we might be able to imagine an alternative methodology, a sort of *halakhah* or law or ethics that functions without problematic analogical thinking. Yet such an imaginary thing belongs to the realm of thought experiment or fantasy. In the real world of intellectual practice, all these modes of thought depend on analogies drawn from very old canonical texts for their growth, development, and creative energy. Yes, analogies can at times be forced and unpersuasive, and they may never yield absolute certainty; the woodchopper, at the end of the day, is not exactly the same thing as an artificial respirator, and the comparison of the one to the other is bound to leave some of us unconvinced. The halakhic analogies we have been dealing with here can claim persuasiveness only because of the controversial (if congenial) interpretive assumptions with which our authors have approached the texts. But that is the case with *all* analogies: the only way to solve "the problem of importance" is by way of an assumption or assertion or translation that enables us to argue that the similarities between the source case and the target case outweigh the differences between them. At times, perhaps frequently, those who argue from analogy do not make explicit the assumptions upon which their argument rests. Louis Newman has criticized Jewish bioethicists for not doing so, yet he takes pains to reject the suggestion that those bioethicists stop studying – and, necessarily, drawing analogies from – Jewish texts, even as he calls upon the scholars to pursue their work more critically and reflectively.[109] And that is precisely my point with respect to *halakhah*. The gaps, technological and otherwise, between the traditional texts and the contemporary issues that confront the halakhist may be significant, but their existence should not deter him or her from the study of Torah. Indeed, the bridging of those gaps is precisely what the study of Torah, historically considered, is all about.

My second observation has to do with the relevance of all this to our enterprise of progressive *halakhah*. I have mentioned "the liberal critics,"[110] those predominantly Reform and Conservative Jewish writers who doubt or deny that traditional halakhic thought can provide an adequate basis for a contemporary progressive Jewish bioethics. Our study, at the very least, calls their claim into question. If the traditional analogy based halakhic process is capable of supporting an intelligent bioethical discourse, it is also capable of supporting an intelligent *liberal* halakhic discourse. In particular, the CCAR responsum we have considered offers a good example of how Reform rabbis can work within the intellectual boundaries of that process, citing sources and making analogies, and arrive at interpretations of *halakhah* that are fully expressive of liberal values. Indeed, the record of liberal halakhic writing shows that the same is true with respect to the entire range of moral concerns that arise from the contemporary practice of medicine.[111] Reform and Conservative rabbis, working within the discipline we call progressive *halakhah*, have produced a large and vital bioethical literature. In short, while some of the liberal critics do not care for the so-called "formalism" of halakhic thinking, and while others are convinced that *halakhah*, even in its progressive variety, is simply incapable of supporting the particular answers and conclusions that they define as "liberal," our position is that there is no obvious need for liberal Jews to abandon halakhic thinking in favor of some more suitable bioethical methodology.

Our task, therefore, is to continue to emphasize the value of our work and the purposes behind it. We work in this field in the knowledge that one cannot do Jewish bioethics (or "ethics," for that matter) in any convincingly *Jewish* sense of the term without engaging in the study of classic Jewish texts, that provide the material with which we draw analogies to our own experience. And the fact remains that the texts one must study to this end are halakhic texts, sources that have served for centuries as grist for the mill of Jewish legal thought. Since we are liberal Jews, who necessarily read the halakhic texts from a liberal perspective, the conclusions we draw from them will often differ from the conclusions of Orthodox *poskim*, who necessarily interpret the texts from *their* angle of vision. But then, disagreement *(machloket)* has always been an endemic feature of halakhic discourse, and the fact that we disagree with Orthodox authorities over any number of conclusions does not mean that we have abandoned the field of *halakhah* to their exclusive control. On the contrary: it means that we are committed to intellectual openness, to the existence of a plurality of legitimate interpretations, and to the preservation of a *halakhah* that can continue to grow and develop and respond to the needs of every generation.

Notes

1. Louis E. Newman, "Woodchoppers and Respirators: The Problem of Interpretation in Contemporary Jewish Ethics," *Modern Judaism* 10:1 (1990), pp. 17-42.

2. Terrance Sandalow, "Constitutional Interpretation," *Michigan Law Review* 79 (1981), pp. 1033-1072. Newman might well have quoted Sandalow's words at p. 1068: "Constitutional law thus emerges not as exegesis, but as a process by which each generation gives formal expression to the values it holds fundamental in the operations of government."

3. Paul Brest, "The Misconceived Quest for the Original Understanding," *Boston University Law Review* 60 (1980), pp. 204-238.

4. James Boyd White, *Heracles' Bow* (Madison: University of Wisconsin Press, 1985). See, in addition, his *Justice as Translation* (Chicago: University of Chicago Press, 1990) and "What's An Opinion For?" *University of Chicago Law Review* 62 (1995), 1363-1369. White is a leading figure in the "Law and Literature" movement, the adherents of which have contributed much to our understanding of the nature of legal rhetoric and interpretation.

5. Stanley Fish, *Is There a Text in This Class? The Authority of Interpretive Communities* (Cambridge: Harvard University Press, 1980). Fish sharpens his arguments considerably in the essays collected in his *Doing What Comes Naturally: Change, Rhetoric, and the Practice of Theory in Literary and Legal Studies* (Durham: Duke University Press, 1989).

6. Owen Fiss, "Objectivity and Interpretation," *Stanford Law Review* 34 (1982), pp. 739-764.

7. Karl Llewellyn, *The Bramble Bush: On Our Law and Its Study* (New York: Oceana, 1951). For a more thorough explication of Llewellyn's understanding of legal interpretation, see his *magnum opus*, *The Common Law Tradition: Deciding Appeals* (Boston: Little, Brown and Company, 1960), pp. 19-61.

8. Ronald Dworkin, *Taking Rights Seriously* (Cambridge: Harvard University Press, 1977); *A Matter of Principle* (Cambridge: Harvard University Press, 1985); and *Law's Empire* (Cambridge: Harvard University Press, 1986).

9. Newman (note 1, above), p. 18.

10. *Ibid.*, p. 35.

11. The distinction between "killing" and "letting die" is not unique to Jewish thought; it appears frequently in bioethical literature. See Bonnie Steinbock and Alastair Norcross, eds., *Killing and Letting Die, Second Edition* (New York: Fordham University Press, 1994). For a discussion of the distinction, the criticisms lodged against it, and a defense of the distinction against those criticisms, see Tom L. Beauchamp and James F. Childress, *Principles of Biomedical Ethics, Fifth Edition* (New York: Oxford University Press, 2001), pp. 139-143. The distinction between killing and letting die also forms the basis of the position of the American Medical Association (AMA) on the issues under discussion here: the AMA countenances the withholding and withdrawal of futile medical treatment but stands

opposed to euthanasia and physician assisted suicide. See CEJA Report B – A-91, "Decisions Near the End of Life," adopted June 1991 (JAMA. 1992; 267: 2229-2 2 3 3) ; Updated June 1996) h t t p : / / w w w . a m a -assn.org/ama1/pub/upload/mm/codemedical-ethics/221a.pdf (accessed August 13, 2010).

12. See *Hilkhot HaRosh, Moed Katan* 3:97 in the name of his teacher R. Meir of Rothenburg; *Tur* and *Shulchan Arukh Yoreh Deah* 339:2, and *Beit Shmu'el* to *Shulchan Arukh Even Haezer* 17, note 94 (end).

13. Newman (note 1, above), p. 37.

14. I, too, owe much to the writings of these scholars of jurisprudence, and a great deal of my own academic work has attempted to apply their insights to the halakhic context. See, for example, "Torture, Terrorism, and the *Halakhah*," in Walter Jacob, ed., *War and Terrorism in Jewish Law* (Pittsburgh: Solomon B. Freehof Institute of Progressive *Halakhah*, 2010), pp. 13-50; "Narratives of Enlightenment: On the Use of the 'Captive Infant' Story by Recent Halakhic Authorities," in Walter Jacob, ed., *Napoleon's Influence on Jewish Law* (Pittsburgh: Rodef Shalom Press, 2007), pp. 93-147; "Halachah, Aggadah, and Reform Jewish Bioethics: A Response," *CCAR Journal* 53:3 (Summer, 2006), pp. 81-106; "Against Method: On *Halakhah* and Interpretive Communities," in Walter Jacob, ed., *Beyond the Letter of the Law: Essays on Diversity in the Halakhah* (Pittsburgh: Rodef Shalom Press, 2004) pp. 17-77; "Taking Precedent Seriously: On *Halakhah* as a Rhetorical Practice," in Walter Jacob and Moshe Zemer, eds., *Re-Examining Reform Halakhah* (New York: Berghahn Books, 2002), pp. 1-70; "*Halakhah* in Translation: The Chatam Sofer on Prayer in the Vernacular," *CCAR Journal* 51:3 (Summer, 2004), 142-163; "Responsa and the Art of Writing: Three Examples from the *Teshuvot* of Rabbi Moshe Feinstein," in Peter S. Knobel and Mark N. Staitman, eds., *An American Rabbinate: A Festschrift for Walter Jacob* (Pittsburgh: Rodef Shalom Press, 2001), pp. 149-204; "Abortion and the Halakhic Conversation: A Liberal Perspective," in Walter Jacob and Moshe Zemer, eds., *The Fetus and Fertility in Jewish Law* (Pittsburgh, Freehof Institute of Progressive Halakhah, 1995), pp. 39-89; "Responsa and Rhetoric: On Law, Literature, and the Rabbinic Decision," *Pursuing the Text: Studies in Honor of Ben Zion Wacholder* (London, Sheffield Press, 1994), pp. 360-409; and "Halakhah and Political Theory: A Study in Jewish Legal Response to Modernity," *Modern Judaism*, October, 1989, pp. 289-310.

15. See David R. Hiley, James F. Bowman and Richard Shusterman, eds., *The Interpretive Turn; Philosophy, Science and Culture* (Ithaca, NY: Cornell University Press, 1999), p. 1.

16. The proper citation here is Thomas Kuhn's celebrated work *The Structure of Scientific Revolutions* (Chicago: University of Chicago Press, 1970), which famously described the influence of existing "paradigms" of knowledge upon the work of scientists.

17. "Alles Verstehen ist Auslegung"; Hans-Georg Gadamer, *Wahrheit und Methode: Grundzüge einer philosophischen Hermeneutik.* (Tübingen: J. C. B. Mohr, 1975, pp. 366, 375, and 377. See also H.G. Gadamer, *Truth and Method.* Translated by J. Weinsheimer and D. C. Marshall (New York: Crossroad, revised edition, 1989), pp. 307-308: "Understanding always involves something like the application of the text to be understood to the present situation of the interpreter." Gadamer's influence is crucial in the writings of most contemporary hermeneutical theorists, including many who work in the discipline of jurisprudence. See, in general, Gregory Leyh, ed., *Legal Hermeneutics* (Berkeley: University of California Press, 1991) and Menachem Mautner, "Gadamer vehamishpat," *Iyunei Mishpat (Tel Aviv University Law Review)* 23:2 (March, 2000), pp. 367-419.

18. By "liberal" I have in mind those scholars who consciously identify themselves with non-Orthodox movements and whose bioethical writings are exercises in halakhic methodology. Exemplary among these is Elliot Dorff, *Matters of Life and Death: A Jewish Approach to Modern Medical Ethics* (Philadelphia: Jewish Publication Society, 1998). See as well the various essays in Walter Jacob and Moshe Zemer, eds., *Death and Euthanasia in Jewish Law* (Pittsburgh and Tel Aviv: Rodef Shalom Press, 1995). Particularly instructive is the article by Peter Knobel in pp. 27-60 of that volume, an article substantially reprinted in William Cutter, ed., *Healing and the Jewish Imagination* (Woodstock, V.: Jewish Lights, 2007), 171-183. A number – though not all – of these essays argue that active euthanasia or physician assisted suicide are justifiable Jewish responses to terminal illness. While this position clearly runs counter to the accepted traditional consensus, as well as to the position enunciated in most Reform responsa, those authors defend and elaborate their view by means of halakhic reasoning – that is, by appeal to precedential texts.

19. See Benjamin Freedman, *Duty and Healing: Foundations of a Jewish Bioethic* (New York: Routledge, 1999), and Ronald Green, "Jewish Teaching on the Sanctity and Quality of Life," in E.D. Pellegrino and A.I Faden, eds., *Jewish and Catholic*

Bioethics: An Ecumenical Dialogue (Washington: Georgetown University Press, 1999), pp. 25-42. Philip M. Cohen, "Toward a Methodology of Reform Jewish Bioethics," *CCAR Journal* 52:3 (Summer, 2005), pp. 3-21, calls the approaches of these authors "nonhalakhic." In my response to Cohen ("Halachah, Aggadah, and Reform Jewish Bioethics: A Response," note 14, above), I argue that both Green and Freedman work well within the parameters of halakhic discourse.

20. See Newman (note 1, above), p. 37: "Finally, in no sense do I wish to suggest, given the subjective nature of interpretation as I have described it, that Jewish ethicists should quit reading Jewish texts. Rather, it has been my assumption that what makes contemporary Jewish ethics Jewish is its attempt to develop positions which carry forward the views contained within that long textual tradition."

21. See, especially, the following: Daniel Gordis, "Wanted: The Ethical in Jewish Bioethics," *Judaism* 38 (1989), pp. 28-40; Irving Greenberg, "Toward a Covenantal Ethic of Medicine," in Levi Maier, ed., *Jewish Values in Bioethics* (New York: Human Sciences Press, 1986), pp. 124-149; David H. Ellenson, "How to Draw Guidance from a Heritage: Jewish Approaches to Mortal Choices," in Barry S. Kogan, ed., *A Time to be Born and a Time to Die: The Ethics of Choice* (New York: Aldine de Gruyter, 1991), pp. 219-232; Peter Knobel (see note 18, above), and Philip M. Cohen (see note 19, above).

22. Irving Greenberg, of course, is an exception to this rule. He regards himself as an Orthodox rabbi, whether or not the preponderance of today's Orthodox Jews would accept him as such. At any rate, he does not formally identify with one of the liberal Jewish groupings.

23. "Formalism" is a term of art in legal theory. It is generally used to denote the theory that legal decision is determined more or less exclusively by the process of logical deduction from preexisting legal materials. Formalists hold that legal decisions are constrained and determined by the law's rules and systemic procedures, which yield a uniquely correct answer to every legal question. Not all legal method is "formalist." In particular, as we shall see, analogy requires a crucial non-formalist component, since the argument that a particular analogy is compelling demands a judgment that itself is not the product of logical or formal necessity. The real target of these critics' ire, it seems to me, is *legalism*, the very idea that answers should be sought by *any* sort of legal method.

24. "The basic pattern of legal reasoning is reasoning by example"; Edward H. Levi, *An Introduction to Legal Reasoning* (Chicago: University of Chicago Press, 1949), p. 1. "[L]egal argument is often associated with its own distinct method, usually referred to as 'reasoning (or argument) by analogy'"; Scott Brewer, "Exemplary Reasoning: Semantics, Pragmatics, and the Rational Force of Legal Argument by Analogy," *Harvard Law Review* 109 (1996) pp. 923-1028 (quotation at p. 926). "So what is it that lawyers and judges know that philosophers and economists do not? The answer is simple: the Law. They are the masters of 'the artificial Reason of the law.' There really is a distinct and special subject matter for our profession. And there is a distinct method.... It is the method of analogy and precedent"; Charles Fried, "The Artificial Reason of the Law; or, What Lawyers Know," *Texas Law Review* 60 (1981), pp. 35-58 (quotation at p. 57). Richard Posner calls reasoning by analogy "the heart of legal reasoning as conceived by most modern lawyers," even as he criticizes it as having "no definite content or integrity"; *The Problems of Jurisprudence* (Cambridge: Harvard University Press, 1990), p. 86.

25. See Steven J. Burton, *An Introduction to Law and Legal Reasoning* (Boston: Little, Brown and Company, 1985), 59-82, describing "the two forms of legal reasoning," deductive and analogical, that lawyers combine in their work. See also James R. Murray, "The Role of Analogy in Legal Reasoning," *UCLA Law Review* 29 (1982), pp. 833-871 ("Analogy is a vital tool in legal reasoning"; p. 833).

26. See Burton (note 25, above), p. 26.

27. Burton (note 25, above), p. 27.

28. Posner (note 24, above), pp. 99-100, argues that "legal reasoning" is not a method but a language, "a culture, a vocabulary, a set of representative texts and problems." I make a similar point with respect to halakhic reasoning in general in "Against Method" (note 14, above) and "On the Absence of Method in Jewish Bioethics: Rabbi Yehezkel Landau on Autopsy," in Alyssa Gray and Bernard Jackson, eds., *Jewish Law Association Studies XVII* (2007), 254-278.

29. *Olmstead v. U.S*, 277 U.S. 438 (1928).

30. *Ibid.*, at 464-465.

31. The citation is from *Weems v. U.S.,* 217 U.S. 349, 373, an important precedent – analogy – upon which Brandeis relies.

32. *Olmstead* (note 29, above), at 473.

33. Cass Sunstein, *Legal Reasoning and Political Conflict* (Oxford: Oxford University Press, 1996), p. 8. Sunstein sees analogical reasoning as a key element in a democratic society's ability to arrive at what he calls "incompletely theorized agreements": that is, "when people diverge on some (relatively) high-level proposition, they might be able to agree when they lower the level of abstraction" (p. 37). Analogy is thus an example of "bottom-up" thinking, which proceeds from agreed-upon particulars and reaches agreement at a comparatively modest level of abstraction, as opposed to "top-down" thinking that starts from controversial general propositions and therefore has difficulty yielding agreement on particulars (p. 68). For a good example of how such low-level agreement is obtained in a situation of profound disagreement over basic moral principles, see Jonsen and Toulmin (note 34, below), pp. 18-19.

34. Albert R. Jonsen and Stephen Toulmin, *The Abuse of Casuistry: A History of Moral Reasoning* (Berkeley: University of California Press, 1988). The authors defend casuistry against the bad reputation that has attached to it since (in their reckoning) the days of Pascal's strictures against the Jesuits. What Pascal should have attacked, they write, is not casuistry per se but the wrongful use or abuse of the method; hence, the title of the book (see p. 11ff.). A similar note is struck by Richard B. Miller, *Casuistry and Modern Ethics: A Poetics of Practical Reasoning* (Chicago: University of Chicago Press, 1996).

35. Jonsen and Toulmin (note 34, above), p. 7 (emphasis in original).

36. See Lloyd L. Weinreb, *Legal Reason: The Use of Analogy in Legal Argument* (Cambridge: Cambridge U. Press, 2005), p. 66: "[O]n its own the principle is too broad to express the court's holding and requires reference to the analogy to ascertain its true scope. The direction of thought is from the analogy to the principle, rather than the other way around."

37. Jonsen and Toulmin (note 34, above), p. 13. The examples are Michael Walzer, *Just and Unjust Wars: A Moral Argument with Historical Illustrations* (New York: Basic Books, 1977) and Sissela Bok, *Lying: Moral Choice in Public and Private Life* (New York: Pantheon Books, 1978).

38. See Burton (note 25, above), pp. 31-40. The entire second section of his book is devoted to this question. Brewer (note 24, above), p. 951, uses the term "rational

force" to describe the degree to which an analogical inference is judged to be compelling or valid.

39. Sunstein (note 33, above), p. 65.

40. *Lochner v. New York*, 198 U.S. 45, 76.

41. The same point is made by Michael Avraham in his discussion of the traditional rabbinic "hermeneutical principles"; *"Ma-amadan halogi shel darkhei haderash," Tzohar* 12 (2003), p. 20.

42. Weinreb (note 36, above), pp. 12-13: "In law as in life, analogical argument is a valid, albeit undemonstrable, form of reasoning that stands on its own and has its own credentials, which are not derived from abstract reason but rooted in the experience and knowledge of the lawyers and judges who employ it. Some analogical arguments are good and some are bad. Ordinarily, we know how to tell one from the other and are able to reach a fair degree of agreement about which is which. The human capacity for reasoning by analogy presents complex and difficult epistemological questions, but its use is commonplace and, carefully used, its conclusions are generally reliable." Charles Fried (note 24, above) makes a similarly strong claim for analogy.

43. The term is drawn from Brewer (note 24, above), pp. 951*ff*, who classifies the theorists into the categories of "mystics" (those who have strong confidence in the reliability ["rational force"] of analogical argument) and "skeptics," who have little such faith. Brewer places himself firmly in the soft middle ground, in a category he calls "modest-proposal rationalists." I'd place myself there, as well.

44. See Burton (note 25, above), pp. 165-166.

45. I do not wish here to enter the venerable controversy over the precise relation between law and ethics, whether as a general matter or in the context of Jewish observance. For the latter see Avi Sagi, *Yahadut: bein dat lemusar* (Tel Aviv: Hakibbutz Hameuchad, 1998). I have previously touched on the question, at least as it relates to the issue of halakhic judgment and rabbinical decision making. Put briefly, my view is that it is inappropriate to distinguish between the strictly "legal" and the "nonlegal" ("metalegal," "ethical") aspects of the rabbinical decision, inasmuch as the ruling cannot help but draw upon both sorts of consideration. See "Against Method" and "Halachah, Aggadah, and Reform Jewish Bioethics: A Response," note 14, above).

46. For example, is *kal vachomer* an example of an Aristotelian syllogism or an inductive-analogical form of reasoning? Aviram Ravitsky offers a comprehensive summary of the scholarship on the *midot*, primarily that which has taken place among traditional rabbinical authors but also with a look to contemporary academic researchers as well; see his *Logikah aristotalit umetodologikah talmudit* (Jerusalem: Magnes Press, 2009). See also Avraham (note 41, above).

47. See Menachem Elon, *Jewish Law: History, Sources, and Principles*, Translated from the Hebrew by Bernard Auerbach and Melvin J. Sykes (Philadelphia: Jewish Publication Society, 1994), p. 947: "The judgments and the conduct of a recognized halakhic authority are understood to be the result of his profound understanding of the *Halakhah*, his ability to discern the similarities and distinctions between cases, and his sound perception of the spirit and purpose of the Torah."

48. Rashbam ad loc. reads *gemara* in place of *limud*. However, the reading most frequently attested in the MSS and in the *rishonim* is *talmud*. See Dikdukei Soferim ad loc.

49. Rashbam, *B. Bava Batra* 130b, *s.v .lo mipi gemara, velo mipi maaseh*, and *s.v. ad she-yomeru lo halakhah lema-aseh*.

50. See *Rashbam, B. Bava Batra* 130 b, *s.v. beterifot*.

51. *Yad Ramah, Bava Batra* 130b, *s.v. seifa debaraita*, end.

52. *Resp. HaRosh* 78:3.

53. Rashi, *B. Sukah* 28b, *s.v. vetanoyei*. See also *Or Zarua* II, *Hilkhot Sukah*, ch. 304.

54. See *Sefer Me'irat Einayim* to *Shulchan Arukh Choshen Mishpat* 237, no. 1: a public declaration of his wickedness is made in the synagogue.

55. *Shulchan Arukh Choshen Mishpat* 237:1.

56. Rashi, *B. Kidushin* 59a, *s.v ani hamehafekh bechararah*; *Tosafot ad loc., s.v. ani*; and see especially *Chidushei HaRitva, Kidushin* 59a.

57. *Yad, Ishut* 9:17, and see the commentators ad loc.

58. See Rashi, *B. Yevamot* 109b, *s.v. toke`a atzmo ledevar halakhah*, and *Hagahot HaBaCh, B. Yevamot* 109b, no. 2.

59. The dictum is codified in *Yad, Sanhedrin* 23:8 and *Shulchan Arukh Choshen Mishpat* 8:2.

60. *Yad, Sanhedrin* 20:8.

61. *Shulchan Arukh Choshen Mishpat* 10:2.

62. HaMe'iri, *Beit HaBechirah, Yevamot* 109b. For similar sentiments see *Beit HaBechirah, Bava Batra* 130b, although there he does not explicitly mention analogy.

63. A reference, perhaps, to *M. Avot* 2:10. And see Rashi, *B. Avodah Zarah* 27b, *s.v. chiviya derabanan leit leh asuta kelal.*

64. Compare *Shulchan Arukh Yoreh De`ah* 242:9: a student is permitted to issue halakhic rulings while his rabbi is alive, provided that those rulings are clearly attested in written works ("in books and in the rulings of the *geonim*"). He may not, however, "rely upon his own power of argument and analogy." The source for this is *Hagahot Maimoniot, Talmud Torah* 5, no. 2, in the name of R. Meir of Rothenburg.

65. See R. David ibn Zimra (16th century Egypt/Eretz Yisrael), *Resp. Radbaz* 6:2 (1147) and his commentary to *Yad, Sanhedrin* 20:8: all the limitations, including the use of analogy, apply only to the student who has not yet achieved the status of "scholar" (*she-lo higia lehoraah*).

66. *Vekhi mipnei she-anu medamin naaseh maaseh?; B. Gitin* 19a and 37a. The phrase occurs frequently in the responsa literature to the same effect: our analogies can all too easily lead to uncertain conclusions, and it is best not to rely upon them.

67. The authoritative literary sources of *halakhah* have the same status as "competent scholars." See R. Yaakov Reischer, *Resp. Shevut Yaakov* 2:64: "Our rabbis *are* the texts that have circulated throughout the Jewish community." And see note 64, above.

68. Newman (note 1, above) does discuss (at his note 10) a 1969 responsum of Rabbi Solomon B. Freehof, but he cites no other liberal halakhic writings. One of those available to him is found in Walter Jacob, ed., *Contemporary American Reform Responsa* (New York: CCAR, 1987), pp. 138-140. He barely mentions the works of Orthodox halakhists. Though he does (at note no. 30) briefly refer to a decision by R. Moshe Feinstein, he draws this from a secondary source and does not analyze Feinstein's reasoning.

69. The original source for R. Yosef Karo's ruling in the *Shulchan Arukh* is Tractate S*emachot* ch. 1; see also *M. Shabbat* 23:5 and *B. Shabbat* 151b. The Talmudic passage is cited in *Halakhot Gedolot, Hilkhot Avel* (ed. Hildesheimer, v. 1, pp. 444-45); Alfasi, *Moed Katan*, fol. 16b; *Yad, Avel* 4:5; *Hilkhot HaRosh,Moed Katan* 3:75; and by numerous other *rishonim*.

70. See *M. Shabbat* 23:5 and *Yad, Avel* 4:1.

71. Or metaphor. The close relation between metaphor and analogy is addressed in D. Gentner, B. Boedle, P. Wolff, and C. Boronat, "Metaphor Is Like Analogy," in D. Gentner, K.J. Holyoak, and B.N. Kokinov, eds., *The Analogical Mind: Perspectives from Cognitive Science* (Cambridge, Mass: MIT Press, 2001), pp. 199-253.

72. *Semachot* 1:4, in the name of R. Meir; *B. Shabbat* 151b (*baraita*).

73. Isserles's source for much of this material is *Sefer Chasidim,* ch. 723 (ch. 315, Wistinetzki-Freimann ed.)

74. The term *chovel beatzmo* is used in tort law to refer to self-inflicted wounds in general; see *M. Bava Kama* 8:6 and *B. Bava Kama* 90b and 91b.

75. Various halakhists have sought to do just that. R. Eliezer Yehudah Waldenberg suggests that R. Chaninah's promise to the officer, which was not accompanied by any offer of material gain, amounts to mere words and is not considered an "act" for which he would otherwise be held liable; *Resp. Tzitz Eliezer* 17:72, sec. 4. R. Shelomo Luria (16th century Poland), commenting on the story, draws a distinction between a concrete act undertaken to shorten one's life (forbidden) and requesting from others that they take such an action (not forbidden); *Yam shel Shelomo, Bava Kama* 8:59. Presumably, those who hear this request are not obligated to fulfill it; thus R. Chaninah did not give an authoritative instruction that his life be terminated. Finally, we should make note of R. Yaakov Reischer (18th century Germany) in his

Iyun Yaakov commentary to the *Ein Yaakov, B. Avodah Zarah* 18a: it is possible that during times of religious persecution one is indeed permitted to commit suicide in order to escape physical torture that would otherwise lead one to commit heinous sins. (He cites *Tosafot, Gitin* 57b, *s.v.kaftzu kulan*; see also *Tosafot, Avodah Zarah* 18a, *s.v. veal yechavel beatzmo*.) R. Chaninah's refusal to open his mouth to the flames is therefore an expression of his special piety (*midat chasidut*) and not a decision that he was obligated to make. If so, says Waldenberg (*Resp, Tzitz Eliezer* 18:48), the implications of the case of R. Chaninah are restricted to situations of persecution, and his example should not be analogized to a medical context.

76. Jakobovits, *Jewish Medical Ethics* (New York: Bloch, 1959) is to my knowledge the first monograph published in English on the subject. It was subsequently translated into Hebrew as *Harefuah vehayahadut* (Jerusalem: Mosad HaRav Kook, 1966).

77. R. Immanuel Jakobovits, "Badin im mutar lekarev mitato shel choleh no'ash hasovel yisurim kashi," *HaPardes* 31:3 (1956), pp. 16-19.

78. The first part of Jakobovits's article appears in *HaPardes* 31:1 (1956), pp. 28-31.

79. See *Turey Zahav, Yoreh Deah* 339, no. 2 and *Nekudot Hakesef* ad loc.

80. *Shiltey Giborim* to Alfasi *Moed Katan*, ch. 3, folio 16a (*siman* 1237). The answer is "anticipated" because the *Shiltey Giborim* dates prior to the commentators cited in the preceding note.

81. See *Beit Lechem Yehudah, Yoreh Deah ad loc., s.v. mikoach she'omrim*.

82. Nachmanides writes (*Torat Haadam, Shaar Hasakanah*, ed. Chavel, pp. 41-42) that the source of this *mitzvah* is Exodus 21:19, which establishes medicine as a permitted activity (*reshut*; see *B. Bava Kama* 85b). Nachmanides infers that this "permission" is in fact an obligation, inasmuch as we learn from a number of sources that medicine is a sub-species of *pikuach nefesh*, the commandment to preserve human life. His argument is summarized in *Tur, Yoreh Deah* 336, and see *Beit Yosef* ad loc. Rambam (Maimonides; *Commentary to M. Nedarim* 4:4) locates the source of the *mitzvah* in Deuteronomy 22:2 (a midrash on the word *vehasheivoto*; *B. Bava Kama* 81b and *B. Sanhedrin* 73a). Jakobovits implies that each of these sources applies to its own specific medical situation. The Rambam source covers obligatory treatment (medicine that offers a successful or tolerable

outcome), while the Nachmanides theory refers to medical treatment that promises only "to extend his illness and lengthen his suffering." The latter sort of treatment is permissible but not obligatory.

83. Barukh Rabinovitz, Comments in a Symposium on Determining the Moment of Death, *Sefer Asya* 1 (Jerusalem: Rubin Mass, 1979), pp. 190-198. The quotation is at pp. 197-198.

84. Ya'akov Levy, "Davar hame'akev yetzi'at hanefesh," *Noam* 16 (1973), pp. 53-63. The cited passage is at p. 61.

85. On p. 57 of his article (see preceding note), Levy chastises those who would draw conclusions on the basis of these classic halakhic texts in cases where, presumably, "there is no chance of improving the patient's condition." "What self-confidence! Any experienced physician knows how often he has erred in diagnosis and all the more so in prognosis." It is impossible to maintain such self-confidence in the case of a comatose patient who could live on "for weeks or even months."

86. Aristotle, *On Rhetoric*, translated by W. Rhys Roberts (New York: Modern Library, 1954), Book I, Chapter 2, 1356a: "Of the modes of persuasion furnished by the spoken word there are three kinds. The first kind depends on the personal character of the speaker...".

87. One example of his reputation is the book compiled by Dr. Avraham Steinberg, *Hilkhot rof'im urefu'ah: al pi shu"t tzitz eliezer lehagra"i waldenberg* (Jerusalem: Mosad Harav Kook, 1978) / Avraham Steinberg, *Jewish Medical Law: Compiled and Edited from the Tzitz Eliezer*. Translated by David B. Simons (Jerusalem: Gefen, 1980). One of Waldenberg's positions was that of rabbi of Shaare Zedek Medical Center in Jerusalem. Steinberg was the first director of the Schlesinger Institute for Medico-Halakhic Research at Shaare Zedek (http://www.medethics.org.il) and the founder and first editor of the quarterly *Asya* devoted to issues in medicine and *halakhah*.

88. *Resp. Tzitz Eliezer* 13:89.

89. See at notes 79-81, above.

90. *Resp. Tzitz Eliezer* 13:89, sec. 8. The following citation is at sec. 11.

91. *Bereishit Rabah* 96:3 and elsewhere.

92. For a very similar argument see R. Chaim David Halevy, "Nituk choleh she'afsu sikuyav mimekhonat haneshamah," *Techumin* 2 (1981), 297-305. At p. 304 he describes Isserles's example of salt on the tongue as "the perfect analogy" (*hadimayon hashalem*) to the case of the artificial respirator.

93. *Resp. Igerot Moshe, Choshen Mishpat* 2:73.

94. *Resp. Igerot Moshe, Choshen Mishpat* 2:74.

95. The most powerful formulation of this principle would seem to be that of R. Yaakov Reischer (18th century Germany), *Resp. Shevut Yaakov* 1:13: the laws of Shabbat are set aside for the purpose even of extending the life of a *goses*. For his part, Feinstein declares that "everyone accepts" this rule; *Resp. Igerot Moshe, Orach Chayim* 3:69.

96. Note that the Isserles passage does *not* mention pain and suffering as the reason for allowing the removal of impediments to death. Still, one of Isserles's sources *Sefer Chasidim*, ch. 234 does mention pain in relation to the treatment of the *goses;* see above at note 90. *Beit Lechem Yehudah, Yore Deah* 339*, s.v. mikoach she'omrim*, cites the *Sefer Chasidim* passage and is seemingly the first authority to make the connection between removing impediments and the issue of pain and suffering

97. The language Feinstein uses in the responsum indicates Tendler's concern that the permissive ruling in the earlier *teshuvah* might be used to justify withholding medical treatment from the insane, from those in a comatose state, and other cases where the patient lacks sufficient quality of life. By restricting the warrant to discontinue treatment to cases involving pain and suffering Feinstein explicitly rejects the inference. At the same time, he does not categorically reject "quality of life" as a relevant consideration. On the subject in general, see Moshe D. Tendler and Fred Rosner, "Quality and Sanctity of Life in Talmud and Midrash," *Tradition* 28:1 (1993), pp. 18-27.

98. W. Gunther Plaut and Mark Washofsky, eds., *Teshuvot for the Nineties* (New York: CCAR, 1997), pp. 337-361; http://data.ccarnet.org/cgi-bin/respdisp.pl?file=14&year=5754 (accessed September 15, 2010).

99. "This theory" is that of *Shiltey Giborim* (see at note 80, above)

100. The responsum cites the opinions of Waldenberg, Halevy, and Rabinovitz discussed above.

101. See above at note 82. Unlike Jakobovits, the CCAR responsum does not base its conclusions upon the theoretical differences between Maimonides and Nachmanides, since "[b]oth approaches see the obligation to practice medicine as a subset of the more general commandment to save life." According to either theory, goes the argument, that obligation ceases when life cannot be saved.

102. Thus, the language of Maimonides: "whoever is able to save another (*kol hayakhol lehatsil*) and does not do so has violated the commandment: you shall not stand idly by the blood of your neighbor"; *Yad, Rotzeach* 1:14.

103. This refers to the classic distinction between "certain" and "unproven" medical treatments in R. Yaakov Emden's *Mor Uketzi'ah*, ch. 328. See, in general, R. Moshe Raziel, "*Kefiat Choleh Lekabel Tipul Refui*," *Techumin* 2 (1981), at pp. 335-336.

104. Newman (note 1, above), p. 36.

105. The terminology cited is that of Robert A. Ferguson, "The Judicial Opinion as a Literary Genre," *Yale Journal of Law and the Humanities* 2 (1990), pp. 201-219, especially at p. 213*ff*. See also Paul Gewirtz, "On 'I Know It When I See It'," *Yale Law Journal* 105 (1996), at p. 1042: "The typical judicial opinion is marked by a rhetoric of certainty, inevitability, and claimed objectivity, a rhetoric that denies the complexity of the problem and drives to its conclusion with a tone of self-assurance... This rhetoric of certainty seems connected to judges' perceived need to preserve the institutional authority of the court." See also Richard A. Posner, "Judges' Writing Styles (and Do They Matter?)," *University of Chicago Law Review* 62 (1995), at p. 1430.

106. The CCAR responsum is an exception to this observation, since it is a ruling on a specific question that yet takes pains to defend its position against the alternatives. The difference may lie in the nature of liberal *halakhah*, which tends to emphasize the plurality of views within the Jewish legal tradition over the need to locate the one correct answer to a question of Jewish law. On this subject in general, see Mark Washofsky, "Abortion and the Halakhic Conversation: A Liberal Perspective" and "Against Method: On *Halakhah* and Interpretive Communities" (note 14, above).

107. In particular, I would cite the publications of the Dr. Falk Schlesinger Institute for Medical-Halachic Research (http://medethics.org.il.), including the Hebrew Journal *Assia* and the English Collection *Jewish Medical Ethics and Halacha*. Important studies are also available at the website http:jlaw.com/Articles, sponsored by the Center for Halacha and American Law of the Aleph Institute. In addition and number of the publications of the Freehof Institute of Progressive Halakhah (http://www.jewish-law-institute.com/publications.htm, accessed October 11, 2010) deals with medical subjects. See the following volumes: *Death and Euthanasia in Jewish Law* (1995), *The Fetus and Fertility in Jewish Law* (1996), *Aging and the Aged in Jewish Law* (1998).

108. The theory of constitutive rhetoric is developed by Maurice Charland, "Constitutive Rhetoric: The Case of the *Peuple Quebecois*," *Quarterly Journal of Speech* 73 (1987), pp. 133-150; see also his article "Constitutive Rhetoric," in Thomas O. Sloane, ed., *Encyclopedia of Rhetoric* (Oxford: Oxford University Press, 2001), pp. 616-619. The theory departs from the classical rhetorical understanding of the audience as an entity that exists *prior* to the rhetorical act, with its prejudices, interests, and motives already intact and waiting to be persuaded. On the contrary: an audience does not exist prior to the rhetorical act but is in fact constructed by the rhetorical act itself. While Charland uses the theory to analyze acts of political rhetoric, James Boyd White applies it to the language of the law. See his "Law as Rhetoric, Rhetoric as Law: The Arts of Cultural and Communal Life," *University of Chicago Law Review* 52 (1985), at 692-693: "What I have been describing [as rhetoric] is not merely an art of estimating probabilities or an art of persuasion, but an art of constituting culture and community. It is of this kind of rhetoric that I think the law is a branch... .The establishment of comprehensible and shared meanings, the making of a kind of community that enables people to say 'we' about what they do and to claim consistent meanings for it – all this at the deepest level involves persuasion as well as education, and is the province of what I call constitutive rhetoric." See also James Boyd White, *Heracles' Bow* (note 4, above), at pp. 28-59.

109. See note 20, above.

110. See note 21, above.

111. I *have* argued this point in detail; see my "Halachah, Aggadah, and Reform Jewish Bioethics: A Response," note 14, above.

"AN OUNCE OF PREVENTION, A POUND OF CURE"
PREVENTIVE SURGERY AS LEGITIMATE MEDICINE
Audrey R. Korotkin

INTRODUCTION

Julie Miller was a 34-year old physician living in Phoenix, Arizona, and a new mother.[1] Jessica Queller was a 38-year- old television writer.[2] Both were healthy, happy and successful. And, at this relatively young age, both women chose to undergo double prophylactic mastectomy–removal of both breasts in order to prevent cancer.

In Miller's case, it was the discovery of a family history of breast cancer that led to her decision. Her mother had just passed away, a few weeks before Miller gave birth to her daughter. She knew her mother had been diagnosed with breast cancer in her mid-40s, while she was pregnant with Julie, and had undergone successful treatment. But in going through her mother's medical files, Miller discovered that her mother's mother and her mother's two sisters also had suffered from the disease. Queller's mother actually had succumbed to the disease. But for her, the choice was made clear after she learned that she herself had tested positive for the genetic defect that puts many Ashkenazic Jewish women at a much higher risk for both breast and ovarian cancer.

Miller's breast tissue turned out to be free of cancer. Queller's biopsy actually revealed precancerous changes in her right breast. Both women were, and are, completely certain they made the right decision. Neither has ever had any second thoughts.

The decision to undergo prophylactic surgery of any kind–the removal of any healthy organ or tissue from one's body–is of course fraught with emotional challenges and potential physical dangers, all of which affect not only medical choices, but how the *halakhah* views these choices.

In this introduction, as well as in many of the references in this essay, I will paymuch attention to the particular issue of bilateral prophylactic mastectomy (removal of the second breast when one is found to be cancerous) and contralateral prophylactic mastectomy (CPM, removal of both breasts before they show any sign of cancer). I do this for two reasons: first, the medical community's current focus on this procedure; second, the high genetic risk of breast cancer among women of Ashkenazic descent. To be clear, however, the medical and halakhic principles here apply equally to any surgery or medical procedure designed to prevent a disease from developing or spreading *l'hathila* (beforehand), rather than treating it *b'diavad* (after an illness has already been diagnosed). Some examples follow:

> • The M.D. Anderson Cancer Center at the University of Texas recommends prophylactic thryroidectomy (surgery to remove the thyroid before disease strikes) for individuals diagnosed with Multiple Endocrime Neoplasia 2 (MEN2), which is caused by genetic mutation; such surgery could be recommended for children between the ages of 5 and 10 or even infants six months or younger, depending on the specific mutation.[3]
> • Researchers at the Cleveland Clinic and elsewhere indicate prophylactic colectomy may be recommended for some patients at high genetic risk for developing colon cancer.[4]
> • A report by *The Lancet* in February 2010 emphasized the efficacy of carotid endarterectomy (surgery to remove plaque material causing the narrowing of the artery that provides blood to the brain) in patients at risk for stroke and heart attacks.[5]

In exploring the development of *Halakhah* in this area, we shall look at the following issues:

• How we have defined, and how we might re-define, *refuah* (healing) so that our Jewish ethical concepts and our Jewish legal concepts may evolve along with medical technology. Is medicine defined narrowly as saving life or is it a broader response to the pain of a patient?

• The objective halakhic standards with which we are familiar and comfortable, versus the subjective standards we deal with in the face of pain and suffering. What are the models and guidelines for dealing with response to non-life threatening suffering versus response to life-threatening illness?

• The dynamics of the doctor-patient relationship and the decision-making process. How do rabbis understand and respond to the rights of the patient, as well to as the responsibilities of the physician?

• The issue of the at-risk patient. How do we tend to the needs of someone at high(er) risk for illness or disease through family history or genetic predisposition?

• The dilemma for the pastor. When counseling someone whose pain and suffering is both real and reasonable, is it pastorally and halakhically acceptable to support prophylactic treatment?

All of the English translations of texts that originate in the Hebrew and Aramaic are mine except where noted.

PIKUAH NEFESH
THE TRADITIONAL *HALAKHIC* CONCEPT OF HEALING

The American Medical Association Code of Medical Ethics clearly states the responsibility the physician has to maintain the highest standards of medical care:

A physician shall continue to study, apply, and advance scientific knowledge, maintain a commitment to medical education, make relevant information available to patients, colleagues, and the public, obtain consultation, and use the talents of other health professionals when indicated.[6]

The Jewish legal tradition demands remarkably similar professional standards. Traditional halakhic sources define the practice of medicine as "a *mitzvah* that comes under the umbrella of *pikuah nefesh*[7] (the saving of a life). The *Shulhan Arukh* (Y.D. 336:1) states that the *mitzvah* comes from the Torah itself, a commandment that the *Tur*, following the Babylonian Talmud, derives from the Scriptural phrase *"V'rapo y'rapei"* (and he shall cause him to be thoroughly healed) (Ex 21:19).[8] Under this traditional – and, importantly, completely objective – halakhic model, a patient suffering illness or injury is obligated to seek treatment from a trained medical professional, who is similarly obligated to provide medical care. The responsibility of the physician is so great that withholding treatment is considered to be "shedding blood"[9] and the *halakhah* condemns the medical professional who does not refer the patient to another, more competent and more experienced, practitioner of whom he is aware.[10]

Further, according to the *Shulhan Arukh:* "And if he provides treatment by permission of the *Beit Din* and he makes a mistake and causes harm, he is exempt from [judgment from] earthly courts, though liable for heavenly judgment.[11] Nahmanides provides an expanded description of the *mitzvah* of healing, the leeway given to the healer in terms of accountability, and both its halakhic foundation and legal implications: "One can say here that the doctor is like the judge who is commanded to exercise judgment in that, if he makes a mistake without realizing it, he is not punished at all. For as it is said (B. San 6b): 'Lest the judge say, 'Why should I have all this trouble?'[12] [For this reason] Scripture says 'With you in rendering judgment'[13] (II Chr 19:6). He [is expected to] render judgment according to just what he sees with his own eyes."

Nevertheless, if he makes a mistake and it is recognized by the *Beit Din* that the mistake was his alone, in method or knowledge, and as there [in the case of the judge], if he was judging with permission of the *Beit Din,* however, he is exempt he is exempt from human laws of compensation, but he is not exempt from heavenly judgment until he has made good on the damages, and he shall be exiled until death since the mistake and damage was known, or death was caused by his hand. This is also what the *Tosefta* says (B.K. 6:6) regarding the fact that they are exempt from human law but obligated under heavenly law: A master physician who provides treatment with permission of the *Beit Din* is exempt from human law; his judgment will come in heaven. But in all cases if his error was made unknowingly, he is not under any obligation at all, like the judge that is completely exempt from both human and heavenly judgment, as long as he takes care to be appropriately cautious in capital cases and causes no harm through negligence (Nahmanides, *Torat HaAdam, Inyan HaSakanah).*

The above citations emphasize the importance in *halakhah* of *pikuah nefesh,* including the violation of almost any other *mitzvah* to preserve one's own life,[14] to which the Rambam, both sage and physician, adds: "And if he should die rather than transgress [this *mitzvah*] he has risked his own life [and thus committed suicide]." *(Yad, Hil. Yesodei haTorah* 5:1)

Yet we note a parallel theme in halakhic literature that prohibits a Jew from causing himself harm. The *Mishnah* (B. K. 8:6) relates this by way of a rabbinic *ma'aseh:*

> It once happened that a man uncovered the head of a woman in the marketplace. She came before Rabbi Akiva and he obligated him to pay her four hundred *zuz.* He said to him:

"Rabbi, give me more time," and he gave him time. He watched for her, standing at the entrance to her courtyard, and he broke the jug in front of her in which there was an *issar* of oil. She uncovered her head and palmed it and placed her hand on her head. He brought witnesses against her and came before Rabbi Akiva. He said to him: "Rabbi, to such a one I am to give four hundred *zuz*?" He said to him: "You have said nothing. The one who wounds himself, even though he is not permitted to do so, is exempt [from punishment] but if others wounded him, they are liable."

The *Shulhan Arukh* (H.M. 420:31) abbreviates this obligation by focusing on the conclusion of the story: "One who injures himself, even though he is not permitted to do so, is exempt [from a court imposed punishment]; if others injure him, they are liable."

And the Rambam (*Yad, Hil. Hovel u'Mazik* 5:1) states succinctly: "It is forbidden for a person to injure either himself or his fellow." On the surface, Maimonides' statement seems clear and reasonable. Yet we know that all medical treatments contain some sort of risk, whether from infection, allergic reaction, or unforeseen negative outcome of a procedure due to complications or risk factors. We must ask, then: How much risk is too much risk when it comes to seeking healing. How do we determine the proper balance between risk and benefit?

IS IT WORTH THE RISK? THREE HALAKHIC PERSPECTIVES

The above general ruling by Maimonides notwithstanding, the *halakhah* does indeed understand that there are risks inherent in any surgery or course of medical treatment; this is the reason for the hold-harmless language, as Nahmanides noted above.

Andrew Gurman, M.D., vice speaker of the American Medical Association (AMA) House of Delegates, points out that physicians constantly weigh risks and benefits in helping patients to make decisions about a course of treatment:

> The reality is that we, as physicians, sometimes have to talk to people about procedures where death or serious injury are possible complications or outcomes. Certainly there would be a huge ethical issue if death was a predictable or intended outcome, but not if the risks and benefits are being weighed seriously, and the good of the patient is the primary consideration.[15]

This is true as well in the realm of Jewish law: A technique may be halakhically unacceptable as long as it is high risk, unproven and experimental, but over time it may become halakhically acceptable as the rate of success rises and the length of life increases – that is, when benefits begin to outweigh risks. This was the argumentation in favor of permitting heart transplants used by then Israeli Chief Rabbi Issar Yehuda Unterman, speaking to the Congress of Oral Law meeting in Jerusalem in August of 1968,[16] and echoed here by Rabbi Eliezer Yehuda Waldenberg in amending his original ruling against permitting transplants:

> However, all of this is applied when, in any event, the chances for life or death in submitting to a surgery such as this are fiftyf-ifty, but not when there is a greater than even chance that the patient will die as a result of the surgery (Please see what I have written in *Sefer HaHayim,* in which I allude to this point in the explanation that "it is necessary that it be the opinion of the doctors that [the chances of success] are fifty-fifty."[17]

The halakhic perspective (or perspectives) on evaluating

benefit versus risk is crucial to understanding how Jewish law might respond, not only to a case of already-existing illness or injury, but also to the case at interest here; that is, whether the *halakhah* would potentially support preventive treatment such as surgery, which inherently carries risk, to the greater benefit of an at-risk patient's long-term health.

We find three such halakhic perspectives in Rabbi Moshe Raziel's essay, *"K'fiyyat holeh l'kabel tipol rifui"* ("Requiring the Patient to Receive Medical Treatment").[18] The presenting dilemma is this:

> A hospitalized patient is in grave condition, and the doctors say they must perform surgery on him, even though there is doubt in their minds that the operation will be successful. He may even die on the operating table, though without the surgery he surely will die within days. The patient and his family are refusing to give permission for the operation for this reason, and one of the doctors asks for a halakhic opinion on whether it would be permissible for, or even incumbent upon, the doctors to perform the operation despite the family's wishes. He also asks about the merit of the family's position.

Although the main focus of the essay does not pertain to our question here, Raziel does introduce, in section four of the essay, an analysis of the *halakhah* as it pertains to weighing benefit versus risk. The core halakhic text is the talmudic *sugya* found in B. A.Z. 27a-b regarding *hayyei sha'ah,* which is defined as the "life of the hour;" that is, the brief amount of life that may remain for a gravely ill person if left untreated or that may be gained through surgery or some other positive act. The *Gemara*'s discussion springs from the Mishnah on page 27a regarding Jewish interaction with idolators.

Mishnah: We may take monetary medical treatment from the, but not treatment of the *nefesh* (A.Z. 27a).

The *Gemara*'s definitive explanation is that "monetary treatment" refers to veterinary services performed on one's animal and "treatment of the nefesh" refers to medical treatment of the human body, even for a matter that seemingly cannot possibly become life-threatening. But in the *sugya* that follows, the *Gemara* indicates that the Mishnah's statement on the treatment of humans may be qualified, depending on the implications of *hayye sha'ah*. (The following translation is mine with annotations to add clarity.)

Rava said in the name of Rabbi Yohanan (and some say it was Rav Hisda in the name of Rabbi Yohanan): "When a patient might live or might die [if left untreated], we may not accept treatment from [pagan practitioners]. But if he surely will die [without treatment] we may receive treatment from them."[19]

[The *Gemara* asks: Is this really true in a case where he surely] will die? But surely there is [a concern for] *hayye sha'ah*,[a last bit of life that might be taken from him in the pagan's hands]![20]

[The *Gemara* responds:] We do not concern ourselves with fleeting life. And from where do you learn we do not concern ourselves with fleeting life? For Scripture says (II Kings 7), "[There were four men, lepers, outside the gate. They said to one another, 'Why should we sit here waiting for death?] If we decide to go into the town, what with the famine in the town, we shall die there; [and if we just sit here, still we die. Come, let us desert to the Aramean camp. If they let us live, we shall live; and if they put us to death, we shall but die.']" Here [they had] fleeting life, so does this story not imply that we do not concern ourselves with fleeting life [since the lepers chose the risk of being killed immediately by the Arameans rather than live out their *hayye sha'ah* in the desert]?

[The *Gemara*] offers a challenge [to this conclusion with a Baraita]: "One should not have dealings with the *minim*, nor may we receive medical treatment from them [and so endanger] even fleeting life. There was a situation regarding Ben Dama, son of Rabbi Yishmael's sister, who was bitten by a [deadly] snake and Ya'akov of K'far Sekhaniya [who was a heretic,] came to heal him but Rabbi Yishmael would not let him.[21] He [Ben Dama] said to him: 'Rabbi Yishmael, my brother, leave him alone and let me be healed by him, and I will bring a verse from Torah to show you that it is permitted!' But he did not have the chance to finish before his soul departed and he died. Rabbi Yishmael proclaimed over him: 'How fortunate you are, Ben Dama, that your body is pure and your soul departed in purity! For you did not transgress the words of your fellow [sages] who said [relating to *Kohelet* 10:8]: He who breaches a fence[22] will be bitten by a snake.'"

[The *Gemara* responds that this is no proof at all since it deals with Jewish heretics and not pagans:] *Minut* is different because it is attractive; one may become attracted to them.[23] [Furthermore, the *Gemara* points out that in the *Baraita*, Rabbi Yishmael] The Master said "You did not transgress the words of your fellows who would say, He who breaches a fence will be bitten by a snake." But Ben Dama already had been bitten by a snake! [So what had he to fear for another snakebite?]

[The *Gemara* concludes that he risked] being bitten by a snake of the Rabbis [for violating their prohibition], for which there is no remedy at all.

Raziel identifies three different interpretations of this *sugya* in the subsequent halakhic material – and therefore three different ways of calculating risk to benefit.[24]

A. *Tosafot* to *Sugya*
"We do not concern ourselves with fleeting life." But surely we learn in Yoma 85a that we save him from the pile of rubble on Shabbat out of concern for *hayye sha'ah*.[25] Hence, we do concern ourselves. For one can say that [both] here and there we work for his welfare: For there [even] if you are not concerned that he will die, and here [even] if you are concerned that without the treatment from a pagan practitioner he surely will die [still,] in both cases we investigate the certain against what is deemed doubtful.

B. Nahmanides on the *Sugya* and the *Tosafot*
Here, regarding fleeting life that is, [the *Gemara* section that contains this *makhloket*:] 'We do not concern ourselves with fleeting life .... But Scripture says: If we decide to go into the town, what with the famine in the town, we shall die there, etc. Here they had fleeting life, so do we not concern ourselves with fleeting life?'

In my opinion, this refers to a case of doubt as to whether there is even ephemeral life left, not whether we should concern ourselves with the quality of life.

C. *Tosafot* of Rabbi Yeshaya di Trani (13th Century Italy):
In a case where there is doubt whether he will live or die: Regarding the patient who is in doubtful danger of dying, we do not allow him to be treated by them [the pagan practitioners] where we could send him to the Jewish doctor. But if there is no Jewish doctor to be found, we will have him treated by them [the non-Jews] even against his will, as it is explained. (The explanation is that the law says we do not send him for treatment by a non-Jew if there is a Jewish doctor available, but if there is no Jewish doctor around, then

even against his will he must be treated by the non-Jew). But if the patient will indeed die and there is no doctor in the world who can heal him of his sickness, then we seek healing from them and even if there is a Jewish doctor since basically he will die. Hence "we do not concern ourselves regarding *hayye sha'ah*" [that is, we do not refuse pagan treatment even for fleeting life] based on the fear that the pagan will hasten his death.

Here is the way Raziel interprets and summarizes each of these three commentaries:

A. *Tosafot*: One can endanger a limited lifespan in a case where we are in doubt about whether the therapy will lead to a patient's recovery or will kill him immediately. In other words, preserving *hayyei sha'ah* is not more important than the possibility of a cure. If there is a chance you will beat the disease, you can take the risk. Anything would qualify as legitimate medicine provided that there is a chance of a cure.

B. Ramban: If you know for sure that you have only a certain limited lifespan left to you, you cannot accept the danger and risk. Only if you are on death's doorstep and you have nothing left to lose can you do so.

C. *Tosafot* of Rabbi Yeshaya di Trani: It is permissible to take on the risk of treatment in any case, even if it is clear that the treatment will not cure you but will only prolong your life a bit. Buying time is a legitimate medical goal, so the treatment is legitimate medicine.

The views of both the *Tosafot* and Rabbi Yeshaya di Trani point toward a positive halakhic response to prophylactic surgery, though in differing circumstances. The *Tosafot* seems to presume an already advanced stage of disease and would permit radical treatment on even a slim chance for a cure. Rabbi Yeshaya's interpretation, however, is the more useful one for our purposes, since it casts a wide net, broadening the possible scenarios under which one could be guided by his decision. His *heter* would seem, for example, to apply in the case of an at-risk woman who has developed cancer in one breast and chooses to have a bilateral mastectomy, removing both the cancerous breast and the one in which cancer has not yet been found but may (or may not) develop in the future.

While Rabbi Yeshaya's *heter* moves us forward in the evolution of the *halakhah* on this matter, even he still presumes an already existing illness or injury; still grounded in the traditional halakhic definition of *refuah*, he does not account for the person who may be seeking preventive treatment for an illness or injury that does not yet –and may never– exist. This advance in halakhic thinking only came five centuries later.

YA'AKOV EMDEN: CHANGING THE DEFINITION OF *REFUAH*

Up until now, our halakhic conversation has been rooted in the traditional definition of *refuah* as falling under the umbrella of *pikuah nefesh*; that is, medical treatment is given for illness or injury to preserve one's life. If we accept this definition as still valid, then

we must automatically conclude that prophylactic surgery has no medical value, because it is not treating an already-existing illness or injury.

But let us suppose that this definition is no longer adequate. Immunization to prevent illness, for example, is widespread and generally accepted as legitimate medicine. Many school districts require children to be vaccinated against measles, mumps, rubella, and smallpox before they can attend school; likewise, vaccines against diseases such as malaria and cholera are often required when one travels abroad. Judaism looks favorably upon such preventive measures, according to Jewish medical ethicist Elliot N. Dorff:

It would be a violation of Jewish law, for example, for a Jew to refuse to be inoculated against a disease, at least where the inoculation has a proven track record of effectiveness. Jews, on the contrary, have a positive duty to have themselves and their children inoculated against all diseases where that preventive measure is effective and available.[26]

Twice in recent years, the CCAR Responsa Committee has upheld this view as based in *Halakhah*: in December, 1990, in ruling that a religious school family's refusal to vaccinate their child against prevalent childhood diseases is "misguided and outside the realm of Jewish tradition;"[27] and more recently in ruling that "a congregation is entitled, should it so choose, to adopt a rule that requires immunization of students before their admission to religious school," provided there are exemptions for those for whom the inoculations would pose a particular medical risk.[28]

Since we have accepted that legitimate *refuah* may include prevention of disease *l'hathila* in addition to treating it *b'diavad*, we must now consider how this broadens the halakhic definition of medicine and how this evolution in halakhic reasoning relates specifically to the issue of prophylactic surgery. Here we look at a critical passage in which the 18th-century German *posek* Rabbi Ya'akov Emden ben Zvi truly and consciously redefines and expands the legal understanding of *refuah*. We begin with the core text from the *Shulhan Arukh* (O. H. 328:10) on life-preserving situations that override Sabbath restrictions:

For any patient whose doctors say is in danger, even from a skin disease, we desecrate the Sabbath on his behalf. If one doctor says it is necessary [to desecrate the Sabbath to treat this patient] and another says it is not necessary, we desecrate the Sabbath [to treat him]. And there is one [authority] who says one need not be an expert [to make this assessment] because every single person is considered an expert to some extent, and in cases where there is a question of doubt regarding human life, we are lenient.

To this, Avraham Gombiner presented the 17th century Polish custom in his commentary, *Magen Avraham*. It offers a clarification based on the rulings of the RaDBaZ[29] and invoking the responsibility of the physician even over the protests of the patient:

"One doctor says it is necessary [to desecrate the Sabbath]" If the patient does not want to accept the medical treatment, we force him to do so. If the patient says, "I need such and such treatment" and the physician says it is not necessary, we listen to the patient. But if the doctor says that this same treatment would cause him no harm, we listen to the doctor.

Rabbi Ya'akov Emden ben Zvi[30] In his *Mor u-Ketzi'ah* commentary on the *Tur* and the *Shulhan Arukh,* Emden clearly moves the focus of the argument away from the responsibility of the physician, as emphasized by the *Magen Avraham*, and toward the feelings of the patient. In doing so, he clarifies the grounds on which an ill person may or may not be forced to undergo treatment on the Sabbath. He must submit, writes Emden, if his resistance is based on his piety; that is, if "he is stringent in his observance and fears violating the prohibitions on desecrating the Sabbath." But if the patient's resistance is because he is "mistrustful of the treatment itself . . . [and] he is supported by a doctor," the patient's wishes hold sway and he is not forced to undergo the treatment.

Up to this point, Emden has adhered to the parameters presumed by the *Shulhan Arukh:* The patient's life is at stake, immediate treatment is necessary to try and save him, and the

Halakhah permits this to be done even on the Sabbath in the name of *pikuah nefesh*. Now, however, Emden consciously takes a bold step forward, moving outside of these traditional halakhic parameters and into previously uncharted territory:

But those who choose to enter into a situation of possible danger *(safek nefashot)* in order to relieve themselves of great suffering *(k'dai l'hatzil atzmam m'isurim kashim)* ... for example, those who undergo surgery because of a stone in a cyst or vein or the kidney stone that is causing them pain as severe as death *(b'tza'ar kashe kamot)*, may God save us *(rahmana leitzlan)*, we permit them to do it as they desire, without protest, because a number of times we have done this and it has healed them. In any event [however], they ought to think carefully about this.

By introducing this situation and offering this *p'sak halakhah,* Emden has opened a door to an entirely new way of understanding *refuah*. With these words, he has:

• Introduced a life-threatening situation where one did not exist, since the patient's pain was severe but not life-threatening;
• Accepted palliative treatment of severe pain as legitimate medicine;
• Moved the entire context of the *refuah* discussion from objective standards of illness and healing to the subjective standards of pain and its alleviation – subjective because only the individual patient can make the determination of how much pain he or she can tolerate before it becomes too great to bear and feels "like death."

Given that we are now dealing with subjective, patient-centered standards of pain, we must now ask: Can we not take Emden's conclusion further? Might it include, say, the alleviation of emotional pain and suffering for a patient whose anguish over her at-risk status is *"kamot,"* like a death sentence to her, even if disease has not yet (and may never) appear in her body, so long as her fear and anguish are reasonable as well as real? Or would that be considered too much of a stretch of logic?

"I don't think you're stretching it," says Dr. Julie Miller,[31] breast radiologist at Central Baptist Hospital, Lexington, Kentucky. "Sitting in this job on a daily basis, I don't think it's a stretch at all." Miller notes that is especially true of women who already have been diagnosed and treated for cancer in one breast and who are at a higher risk of cancer in the other:

> "Every woman that I see with breast cancer if she's had a complex mammogram or had multiple biopsies or has had a ton of narrowly missing and then I catch her in the net, now we have a cancer I almost wish that those women would choose [prophylactic] mastectomies. Because notoriously, when I have to work them up in six months or a year, for something that may turn out to be fine, it's like posttraumatic stress disorder. They literally collapse on me, because now they feel like they will have to do it again, and they feel they barely made it through the first time. And they just completely unravel, most of them do."[32]

Miller also notes that prior personal history of cancer is not the only reason for choosing prophylactic surgery; family history also plays a major factor. In these cases, she says, she will refer patients for genetic counseling – an added, crucial element in determining both the objective risk to the woman, and the added, subjective element of emotional pain and distress.[33]

Miller's recommendations reflect those of the Mayo Clinic, whose staff offers prophylactic mastectomy as a risk-reducing strategy for women with the following conditions that greatly increase the risk of developing breast cancer:

• Already had cancer in one breast, with a strong family history of the disease;

• A family history of breast cancer, such as a mother, sister, or daughter with beast cancer, especially if they were diagnosed before age 50;

• Positive results from gene testing, indicating the presence of the BRCA1 or BRCA2 mutation;

• Early signs of cancer in the breast, such as precancerous or abnormal cells in the milk-producing glands;

• Radiation therapy in the chest before age 30;

• Dense breasts and strong family history or precancerous conditions[34]

RISK ASSESSMENT: THE CASE FOR GENETIC SCREENING

Like the traditional *halakhah*, medical decisions made on benefit-to-risk assessments begin with objective research and statistical analysis. For physicians attempting to design a course of treatment, genetic screening can be an indispensable tool for determining not only objective risk but whether the subjective emotional stress, as noted above, meets the criteria of being both real and reasonable.

Shannon Morrill-Cornelius, certified genetic counselor at Central Baptist Hospital in Lexington, Kentucky, says most referrals come to her through a patient's primary-care physician or obstetrician who has identified something of concern in the family history, though some patients are self-referred and are not required to submit a request through a physician.[35] About half her patients, she says, are currently undergoing cancer care or have had cancer in the past, and genetic counseling has been recommended. The reason? It is crucial for the patient and her family to find out if a genetic risk exists. "If you've already had breast cancer and haven't had a bilateral mastectomy, the risk for another cancer is 40 to 60 percent for someone with a BRCA mutation," says Morrill-Cornelius.[36]

The significance of these BRCA mutations is summed up in the following medical report:

Since the early 1970s, doctors and scientists have known that between 5 and 10 percent of breast cancer cases are caused by inherited factors. In 1994, they discovered a single gene that, when mutated, appeared to greatly increase a person's chances of developing breast cancer. The discovery of this gene BRCA1 was quickly followed by the discovery of another gene BRCA2 that also predisposes people to breast cancer. In the intervening years, researchers have discovered that mutations in these genes account for the majority of not only hereditary breast cancers but hereditary ovarian cancers as well, and that these mutations are more common in people of Ashkenazi Jewish descent than in other groups.

Although the BRCA1 and BRCA2 genes appear to be similar in function, they are located on different chromosomes, and each, when mutated, confers varying degrees of risk, not only for inherited breast and ovarian cancer but for other types of cancer as well. The types of cancer associated with mutations in the BRCA1 and BRCA2 genes are as follows:

• BRCA1. Mutations in the BRCA1 gene appear to increase an individual's risk for breast, ovarian, prostate, and possibly colon cancer.

• BRCA2. Mutations in the BRCA2 gene appear to increase an individual's risk for breast (male and female), ovarian, prostate, and pancreatic cancers. In addition, researchers suspect that defects in this gene carry with them an increased risk for cancer of the lung, larynx (voice box), and skin; more studies are, however, needed to confirm these associations.[37]

According to this report (and many others), a BRCA mutation will exponentially increase the chance of developing various cancers: For breast cancer, the risk increases from 12.5% of the general population to 55–85% for those with a BRCA1 mutation and 33–86% for those with a BRCA2 mutation. Similarly, the risk of ovarian cancer rises from 1.43% of the general population to 28–44% for those with a BRCA1 mutation and 10–30% for those who carry a BRCA2 mutation.[38]

A more recent cancer study in the United Kingdom points out that most breast cancers occur by chance, and only about 5 out of every 100 cases are related to a known inherited breast-cancer gene. That same study, however, notes that Ashkenazi Jewish women (i.e., those of Central or Eastern European descent) are approximately ten times more likely to carry the genetic defect than women in the general population – about one in 40, or an estimated 2.3 percent of the Ashkenazi female population. For those women, their lifetime risk of developing breast cancer could reach as high as 80 percent, though this risk can vary among families and can be affected by other genetic markers as well as by lifestyle and environmental exposure to carcinogens.[39] Such exponentially high risk creates substantially more fear – fear that is, for this population, both reasonable and real. It also creates the opportunity for the physician the offer the option of bilateral prophylactic mastectomy – both prior to the potential onset of cancer and after cancer has already been diagnosed in one breast – as well as prophylactic oophorectomy, the removal of ovaries.

GENETICS AND OPTIONS

According to the the National Cancer Institute of the U.S. National Institutes of Health a woman with a BRCA1 or BRCA2 mutation that takes no preventive action faces a "60 to 85 percent chance of developing breast cancer and a 15 to 65 percent of developing ovarian cancer by age 70,"[40] Because of significant distinctions in the characteristics of these two genetic mutations as noted above, however, physicians may recommend to such at-risk women different options for prophylactic treatment.

"If you have a BRCA1 mutation, those cancers tend to be [hormone] receptor-negative," says genetic counselor Morrill-Cornelius. "There's nothing we can do to decrease the risk of those cancers, and they also tend to be pretty aggressive, so in those cases we do more strongly suggest that they have a [prophylactic bilateral] mastectomy.... [O]ur BRCA2 patients .... tend to have more hormone-receptor positive breast cancers. So if you do a total hysterectomy and take the ovaries out in a woman who's 40-ish, you're putting her into menopause. Even if you give her small amounts of estrogen therapy to sort of treat the symptoms of menopause, which we do, you're going to put her into surgical menopause. You no longer have that estrogen pump in the body, and if the breast cancers that she's at risk for feed on estogen, which is what estrogen-receptor positive means, then you've dramatically reduced the risk of breast cancer, by about 50 percent."[41]

Morrill-Cornelius also notes that, with a BRCA2 mutation that is estrogen-positive, women may have other options beyond immediate prophylactic surgery: "We also have medications like Tamoxifen and Evista that we can give those woman that block estrogen receptors in the body, and block that pathway, and that further reduce the risk for breast cancers. So in our BRCA2 positive patients, we can bring the risk down to a level where we're a little more comfortable screening as an option."[42]

Morrill-Cornelius reports that, in her practice, about half the patients that test positive for the BRCA2 genetic mutation choose prophylactic mastectomy immediately. The other half opt initially for close screening, including regular mammography and MRIs, but within two years approximately 50 percent of them also undergo prophylactic mastectomy.[43]

Genetic screening – assessed along with family medical history, lifestyle, and environmental factors – can play a major role in the decision-making process a woman and her physician undergo in assessing risk and prescribing treatment. But Morrill-Cornelius warns that today's genetic tests have limitations. "We know two genes are strongly associated with breast and ovarian cancer. We know that there are dozens of genes in the breast cancer pathway, and we haven't figured them all out yet. And the bigger problem is that we don't know how they interact with each other. So because you're not testing them all together, you're not going to get a full picture of risk,"[44] says Morrill-Cornelius. Someone with a clear family history of cancer, then, may not test positive, not because there is no genetic link but because that genetic link has not yet been identified.

PROPHYLACTIC MASTECTOMY: BENEFITS AND LIMITATIONS

Family history, genetic abormality, previous personal cancer history, self-image, emotional distress – all of these may factor into a woman's decision whether or not to undergo prophylactic mastectomy. And the physical and/or emotional anguish she undergoes in coming to this decision may indeed be both real and reasonable – the subjective parameters we have, based on Emden's ruling, set forth for halakhic permissibility.

Yet we must keep in mind that each woman's circumstances are unique; halakhically, then, we must carefully evaluate not only each woman's emotional state of mind but her actual risk, as well as the nonsurgical alternatives that may be available to her, before we can determine whether she would meet these criteria. The medical community likewise has recently expressed concern on this very issue through the National Comprehensive Cancer Network (NCCN), a not-for-profit alliance of 21 top cancer treatment centers across the United States:

> When prophylactic mastectomy is being considered, the NCCN Guidelines note that the small benefits must be balanced with the risk of recurrent disease from the known breast cancer, the psychological and social issues associated with bilateral mastectomy, and the overall risks of contralateral mastectomy.... NCCN Guidelines Panel suggests that high risk women considering a prophylactic mastectomy should be evaluated by a multidisciplinary team and counseled on the risks of the procedure."[45]

Of great concern to the NCCN is the accelerating rate of contralateral prophylactic mastectomy (CPM) --that is, the removal of a presumably healthy breast at the same time a cancerous breast is removed --also recently reported to the public by the support and advocacy group Susan G. Komen for the Cure.[46] Komen cited a recent *Journal of Clinical Oncology* study of more than 150-thousand breast cancer patients, that showed that "the overall rate [of those patients choosing CPM] significantly increased from 1.8% in 1998 to 4.5% in 2003.[47] Likewise, rate for patients undergoing mastectomy significantly increased from 4.2% in 1998 to 11% in 2003" The question for the medical community, as well as for us, is whether this growing number of women have truly assessed risk versus benefit in choosing CPM.

This is an especially crucial question in light of a February 2010 report from the University of Texas's prestigious M.D. Anderson Cancer Care Center showing that "Contralateral prophylactic mastectomy (CPM), a preventive procedure to remove the unaffected breast in patients with disease in one breast, may only offer a survival benefit to breast cancer patients age 50 and younger, who have early-stage disease and are estrogen receptor (ER) negative,[48] a select group of women that represent less than 10 percent of the breast cancer population."[49] The press release noted, however, that the study's researchers, Isabelle Bedrosian, M.D., and George J. Chang, M.D., "expect that future research will show increased survival benefit with longer follow-up in the population, as a patient's likelihood of getting a second breast cancer increases with time. . . . Therefore, for some additional breast cancer patients, CPM may very well be a medically appropriate option.[50]

Significantly, however, this M.D. Anderson study did not capture information on either family history or BRCA status[51] – two major factors in the development of breast cancer among Ashkenazic women that, as we have seen, put them at exponentially greater risk and make the threat of the disease (using our halakhic standards) both real and reasonable. Two significant factors according to the Society of Surgical Oncology, may lead the physician to recommend bilateral prophylactic mastectomy for women without a breast cancer diagnosis, as well as CPM for women with a current or previous breast cancer diagnosis.[52]

So far, we have reviewed many of the benefits associated with bi-lateral prophylactic mastectomy and CPM, particularly for younger women with a genetic mutation, family history, previous cancer history, and/or whose cancer is genetic-receptor negative and who thus lack alternatives to surgery. For them, such surgery not only can provide preventave care, it can also alleviate tremendous emotional anguish over the prospects of developing breast cancer once or again. Physicians warn, however, that beyond the inherent risks of any surgical procedure, consideration of prophylactic mastectomy must include its drawbacks and risks, among which are the following:

1. Many women may overestimate the risk of a woman developing a second cancer. The Society of Surgical Oncology urges full examination of alternative, non-surgical therapies and notes that prophylactic surgery may not decrease mortality rates from the disease.[53]

2. Physicians also "may over-estimate the risk of a contralateral breast cancer," according to a recent report by Susan G. Komen for the Cure, and a doctor's recommendation to have a CPM can be an important factor[54] – perhaps the most important factor – in a woman's decision to have a CPM.[55]

3. Some women may be responding to false warnings. The same Komen report cited studies that link increased use of magnetic resonance imaging (MRI) to rising rates of CPM.[56] But although MRIs can show more detail of a malignancy or potential malignancy, the reports warn they also generate a high rate of false positives, thus possibly skewing the decision-making process between a patient and a physician.

4. Mastectomies do not completely eliminate the chance of developing breast cancer in the future, as some breast tissue remains.

5. Some women may not be exploring nonsurgical options appropriate to their condition. According to the American Society of Clinical Oncology's report on CPM, "[B]ecause hormone therapy reduces the risk of contralateral breast cancer for patients with ER-positive breast cancer, we anticipated that CPM rates would be lower for such patients; however, our data did not show this expected finding."[57]

Taking all these factors into account and adequately assessing benefit to risk are incumbent upon both patient and physician in this decision-making process.

CONCLUSION: DOCTORS, PATIENTS, PASTORS, AND DECISIONS

Rabbi Ya'akov Emden, by affording the patient new power to make choices based on subjective criteria such as pain and suffering, has provided new insight into the evolving halakhic perspective on medical decision-making; new opportunities to broaden the definition of *refuah* based on this evolution; and new challenges to doctors, patients and clergy involved in the process. Whereas each patient's situation is subjectively unique, he or she still has the obligation to seek out all available and appropriate objective information to make an informed decision.

Significantly, the medical community and the halakhic community share the view that doctors and patients must work together to fully weigh the risks and benefits of prophylactic mastectomy, or any other procedure, to determine what constitutes true *refuah* and legitimate medicine.

We rabbis, too, have a role to play; for whereas the physician or other medical-care professional is considered the expert in matters such as assessing family history, genetic markers, and nonsurgical alternatives, we as clergy can assist a woman in recognizing the role that factors like self-image and self-worth, familial pressures, and her emotional state may be playing in her decision-making process, helping to ensure that her concerns are both real and reasonable.
In doing so, we recognize that halakhic concepts about *refuah* have changed and evolved over time, just as *Halakhah* in general has evolved–confronting, and adapting to changes and advancements in society, culture, science, and medicine. The *Halakhah* no longer accepts as adequate the traditional, and purely objective, approach to *refuah* as curing an illness or healing an injury; it now acknowledges that preventive and palliative care – including such subjective notions as physical pain and emotional suffering – play an important role in contemporary medicine.

As rabbis and pastors, we will, no doubt, be faced with helping our congregants make important, life-changing, and even life-endangering decisions about how they choose to live and how they wish to die. Understanding that we can incorporate developments and evolution in halakhic thinking in our work will help us keep ourselves and our congregants ever closer to the comfort and the embrace of Jewish tradition.

Notes

1. Julie Miller, M.D., interviewed by author, Lexington, Kentucky, February 17, 2010.

2. Holly Lebowitz Rossi, "The BRCA Gene: A Positive Test, A Personal Choice, Q&A," *Forward*, April 4, 2008, http://www.forward.com/articles/13020/ (accessed February 17, 2010).

3. "Multiple Endocrine Neoplasia 2 (MEN2)," http/www.mdanderson.org/patient-and-cancer-information/cancer-information/cancer-types/m ultiple-endocrime-neoplasia/men2.html (accessed April 7, 2010).

4. J.M. Church, "Prophylactic colectomy in patients with hereditary nonpolyposis colorectal cancer," abstract, December 1996, http://www.ncbi.nlm.nih.gov/pubmed/9017106 (accessed April 8, 2010). Also see Sapna Syngal, Jane C. Weeks, Deborah Schrag, Judy E. Garber, and Karen M. Kuntz, "Benefits of Colonoscopic Surveillance and Prophylactic Colectomy in Patients with Hereditary Nonpolyposis Colorecta Cancer Mutation," *Annals of Internal Medicine of the American College of Physicians-American Society of Internal Medicine*, vol. 129, no. 10, November 15, 1998, pp. 787-796. The participating researchers come from Brigham and Women's Hospital, Dana-Farmer Cancer Institute, Harvard Medical School; and Harvard School of

Public Health, Boston, Massachusetts.

5. "Carotid Stenting Not As Effective at Preventing Stroke or as Safe as Standard Surgery in the Short-Term," *The Lancet*, quoted in Larry Husten, "Carotid endarterectomy beats stenting in first results from ICSS," February 25, 2010, http://cardiobrief.org/2010/25/carotid-endarterectomy-beats-stenting-in-first-results-from-ICC S/ (accessed April 8, 2010).

6. AMA Code of Medical Ethics, Principle V.
http://www.ama-assn.org/ama/pub/physician-resources/medical-ethics/code-medi cal-ethics/pr inciples-medical-ethics.shtml (accessed July 21, 2010).

7. *Tur, Yoreh Deah* 336; see also *Shulhan Arukh, Yoreh Deah* 336:1.

8. Bavli, Berakhot 60a. The *Gemara* cites Abbaye, who refers to a teaching from the School of Yishmael.

9. *Shulhan Arukh, Yoreh Deah*, 336:1.

10. See Note 7, above.

11. /ohna hbhsc chhju ost hbhsn ruyp 'ehzvu vgyu 's"c ,uarc tphr otu See Note 9, above.

12. Such a man may refuse to serve as a judge if he fears punishment for making a mistake.

13. That is to say, the verdict rests with the judge as long as he judges fairly and honestly the case in front of him; as long as he does this, he has no fear of retribution or punishment.

14. The *Gemara* of the San. 72a, records a teaching of Rabbi Yohanan in the name of Rabbi Shimon ben Yehotzadak that, given the choice between death and sin, an Israelite may choose any transgression except idolatry, incest and murder. The *Gemara* bases this on its interpretation of Leviticus 18:5, You shall keep my laws and precepts which, if a man shall do them, he shall live by them --"Live by them," says the *Gemara*, "and not die by them."

15. E-mail correspondence with Dr. Andrew Gurman, February 24, 2010.

16. I.Y. Unterman, "Points of *Halakhah* in Heart Transplantation," *Noam* 13, 1970, pp. 1-9, referenced in Fred Rosner, *Modern Medicine and Jewish Ethics*, 2nd ed., New York, 1991, p. 289.

17. Eliezer Waldenberg, *Responsa Tzitz Eliezer*, vol. 10, no. 25:5. The issue of when death occurs has been a major obstacle, and a major source of objection, to organ transplantation but is beyond the scope of our discussion.

18. Moshe Raziel, *"K'fiyyat holeh l'kabel tipol rifui,"* *Techonim*, vol. 2, 1981.

19. Rashi explains: Here have here a case where the person will surely die if left untreated and there is no Jewish physician available to treat him. So we allow the pagan to provide treatment since, after all, there is the possibility he might help.

20. Rashi: "For the pagan practitioner might hasten his death when he might have lived a day or two [without the treatment]." Presumably, then, it would be better not to let the pagan touch him so at least he would have a little time left to live.

21. A *Baraita* previously cited by the *Gemara* on page 17a identifies Ya'akov of K'far Sekhaniya as a min, a sectarian or heretic deemed to be an idol worshiper.

22. Rashi: "That is, he who transgresses the words of the sages" – meaning their rules that constitute a "fence" around the Torah to prevent transgression of biblical commandments.

23. Presumably, then, one is never permitted to seek treatment from a heretic, but the same may not be true of a pagan.

24. In the following sections the Hebrew is Raziel's and the English translations of the text and his essay are mine.

25. From the *Gemara*'s discussion on 85a on the *Mishnah* on 83a regarding the saving of a life taking precedence over Sabbath restrictions: /"'[I]f he is found alive one should remove the debris [that traps him]' that's so obvious! No, the statement is necessary to show it applies even in a situation of *hayye sha'ah*, when he has only a short time to live."

26. Elliot N. Dorff, *Matters of Life and Death: A Jewish Approach to Modern Medical Ethics*, Philadelphia, 1998, p. 253.

27. "Refusal of Immunization," in Walter Jacob, *Questions and Reform Jewish Answers: New American Reform Responsa*, 1990, pp. 234-235.

28. Mark Washofsky (ed.), Responsum 5759.10, "Compulsory Immunization." Not yet in print; available online at http://data.ccarnet.org/cgi-bin/respdisp.pl?file=10&year=5759.

29. David ben Shlomo ibn Zimra (@1479-1573) Spain, Safed; Chief Rabbi of Egypt

30. The translation is mine, as is the boldface type for emphasis.

31. Miller interview.

32. Ibid.

33. Ibid.

34. "Prophylactic Mastectomy: Breast Cancer Prevention for High-risk Women," November 24, 2009. http://www.mayoclinic.com/health/prophylactic-mastectomy/WO00060 (accessed February 8, 2010).

35. Shannon Morrill-Cornelius, interviewed by author, Lexington, Kentucky, March 24, 2010.

36. Ibid.

37. Kathleen Fergus, MS, CGC, and Jill Simonsen, "Genes Can Cause Breast and Ovarian Cancer," last update August 24, 2000. http://www.genetichealth.com/BROV_Gen_of_BROV_Cancer.shtml (accessed February 8, 2010). I added the boldface type for emphasis on the particular Jewish genetic connection.

38. Ibid.

39. "Is There a Link Between Breast Cancer and Jewish Origin?" Cancer Research UK, updated June 19, 2009. http://www.cancerhelp.org/uk/about-cancer/cancer-questions/is-there-a-link-betw een-breast-c ancer-and-Jewish-origin-? (accessed February 8, 2010). A similar study published in the *New England Journal of Medicine* on May 15, 1997, reached the same conclusion in a study of more than 5,300 Ashkenazi Jewish men and women. See "The Odds of Having Abnormal Breast Cancer Genes," last modified on August 7, 2008, http:/www.breastcancer.org/genetic/odds_abnrml_genes.jsp (accessed February 8, 2010).

40. "Preventative Surgery Can Reduce Cancer Risk in Women with BRCA Gene Mutations." http:/www.cancer.gov./clinicaltrials/preventive-surgery/0502 (accessed September 1, 2009).

41. Morrill-Cornelius interview.

42. Ibis.

43. Ibid. Similar clinical experiences are reported by Jennifer Litton, M.D, "Women with BRCA Mutation, Or Worry, Most Likely to Undergo Prophylactic Mastectomy," M.D. Anderson News Release, March 9, 2009. http://www.mdanderson.org/newsroom/news-release/2009/women-with-BRCA-mutation-orworry-most-likely-to-undergo-prophylactic-mastectomy (accessed March 7, 2010).

44. Ibid.

45. "Updated NCCN Guidelines for Breast Cancer Discourages [sic] Prophylactic Mastetctomy in Women Other Than Those at High Risk." http://www.nccn.org/about/news/newsinfoasp?/NewsID=226 (accessed July 14, 2010). The article lists the NCCN member institutions.

46. "Why Are Rates of Bilateral Mastectomies Rising?" http://ww5.komen.org/ContentSimpleLeftaspx?id=6442452097 (accessed June 3, 2010).

47. Todd M. Tuttle, Elizabeth B. Haberman, Erin H. Grund, Todd J. Morris, and Beth A. Virnig, "Increasing Use of Contralateral Prophylactic Mastectomy for Breast Cancer Patients: A Trend toward More Aggressive Surgical Treatment,"

Journal of Clinical Oncology, vol. 25, no. 33, November 20, 2007, published on-line at www.jco.ascopubs.org (accessed July 14, 2010).

48. This would reflect the information provided by Shannon Morrill-Cornelius, who stated above that such estrogen-receptor negative cancers are aggressive and resist treatments such as Tamoxifen or Evista.

49. "Contralateral Prophyactic Mastectomy Associated with Survival in Select Group of Breast Cancer Patients," M.D. Anderson News Release February 25, 2010. http://www.mdanderson.org/newsroom/news-releases/2010/02-25-10-contralater al-prophylactic-mastectomy-associated-with-survival-in-select-group-of-breast-cancer-patients.html (accessed April 7, 2010).

50. Ibid. The survey "used the National Cancer Institute's Surveillance, Epidemiology and End Results (SEER) registry to identify 107,106 breast cancer patients who underwent a mastectomy for treatment, as well as a subset of 8,902 women who had CPM. All the women were treated for stages I -III breast cancer between 1998 and 2003."

51. Ibid.

52. "Society of Surgical Oncology: Position Statement on Prophylactic Mastectomy." http://www.surgonc.org/default.aspx?id=179 (accessed July 20, 2010).

53. Ibid.

54. L.L. Montgomery, K.N. Tran, M.C. Heelan, *et al.*, "Issues of Regret in Women with Contralateral Prophylactic Mastectomies." Annals of Surgical Oncology, 6:546-552, 1999, quoted in *Journal of Clinical Oncology*, note 46 above.

55. "Why Are Rates of Bilateral Mastectomies Rising?" See Note 48, above.

56. Ibid, quoting K.Y Billimoria, A. Cambic, N.M. Hansen, K. P. Bethke,

"Evaluating the Impact of Preoperative Breast Magnetic Resonance Imaging on the Surgical Management of Newly Diagnosed Breast Cancers," *Archives of Surgery*, 142(5); 441-5.

57. Tuttle, *et al.* The author is grateful to Dr. Mark Washofsky for his guidance and support.

COMPULSORY TESTING FOR HIV AND OTHER INFECTIOUS DISEASES
Jonah Sievers

I remember the outbreak of hysteria caused by a newly discovered disease called HIV or AIDS, in the late 1980s. The public discussion of the subject was irrational as could be expected. Among various proposals was the suggestion for compulsory testing for HIV for immigrants and high-risk groups. More recently SARS has frightened people and resulted in the screening of body temperatures of travelers arriving at airports, to identify potential carriers.

In some countries compulsory testing for HIV has become a reality, as for example, Cuba which introduced mandatory testing for HIV for all its citizens. In 2006 President Bill Clinton advocated mandatory testing for countries with a high infection rate.[1] On my recent arrival in the United States, I was required to state that I am not HIV positive; otherwise entrance would have been denied (which is not the case for most countries in the European Union). Elsewhere, opt-out screening has been promoted as recommended by the Centers for Disease Control and Prevention (*Revised Recommendations for HIV Testing of Adults, Adolescents, and Pregnant Women in Health-Care Settings* [September 2006]).[2]

The CDC's revised recommendations state explicitly that whereas health care providers should routinely administer tests for HIV, they may not do them against the patient's wishes, nor may they deny treatment.. The rationale for this ruling is the personal autonomy of the individual. The question of autonomy in general and in bioethics in particular continues to be of interest to us and is discussed constantly by liberal halachists. It needs to be seen alongside Judaism's concern with maintaining health, as Maimonides stated:

> If the body is healthy [it is] because of God's dealings, for behold it is impossible to understand or know of God's intention

and why [this person] is sick. Therefore one needs to distance oneself from things that harm the body and to conduct ones life [in order to] be healthy *(*Yad *Hil. Deot* 4:1*)*.

Corollaries to this position are preventive measures formulated by the *Shulhan Arukh*:

> When life is endangered, it is a *mitzvah* to remove the threat,. guard against it, and to be very alert – "take utmost care and watch yourself" (Deut. 4:9). Anyone who fails to remove it and leaves it, he has transgressed the positive commandment "do not bring bloodguilt [into your house]" (Deut. 22:8 – *Shulhan Arukh* Hosh*en Mishpat* 427:8).

This idea ultimately led to the principle that when life is endangered *(pikuach nefesh)* all, except three commandments are set aside (San. 74a). The tradition also understands that the body is not personal property but leased from God as stated by Maimonides:

> The *Bet Din* must be careful not to accept ransom from a [convicted] murderer, even if he would give all the money in the world, and even if the blood-avenger wants to ransom him [the *Bet Din* shall not accept it], for the soul of this about to be executed individual does not belong to the blood-avenger but to the Holy One, blessed be He *(Yad Hil. Rozeah* 1:4).

This assumption is inconsistent with the notion of autonomy of some in the Reform movement since an individual cannot be autonomous while part of someone else. Practically, one can be autonomous in relation to God but not to the community in which one lives, which by its very nature restricts individual autonomy. This means that our discussion may have no meaning for some Liberal theologians except as a practical matter.

Our halakhic discussion concerning mandatory testing for HIV centers on whether the halakhic concept of the *rodef* applies here. A *rodef* is a person who is threatening the life of another. A *rodef* might be stopped even if that meant taking a life, as the *halakhah* would already consider the endangering individual dead.

As we turn to our issue, one scholar, Rabbi Deichowsky, argues that it is possible to identify high-risk groups (e.g. homosexuals and hemophiliacs), which are in the category of a *rodef.* He also contends that a person or group might be considered a *rodef* even when the danger is in doubt (*safek pikuach nefesh*).[3] Another scholar, G. Freudenthal disagrees on the grounds that (1) the laws of the *rodef* apply only to individuals and not to groups; (2) the victim is passive, whereas in our case the consenting partners transmit the disease.[4] Others rightly reject this notion as "even as one speaks about mutual consent [that is assent to the sexual activity, not] mutual consent to acquire [the disease]."[5]

Freudethal's first objection, however, stands. In addition, I find it hard to accept the notion that the person who causes a *potential* danger *(safek pikuach nefesh)* is a *rodef* as Golinkin has pointed out the original mishnaic text speaks of *immediate* danger.[6] Here I would also hold that the principle of *rodef* does not apply as HIV does not pose an "immediate" threat to others. Unlike other infectious diseases, the transmission of HIV is, in fact, restricted to specific forms of sexual practice, infected blood and contaminated syringes. To state that PWH are *rodfim* would mean that we consider them *per se* as promiscuous and without moral conscience. On the other hand with highly infectious diseases the category of *rodef* might apply.

We should remember that the number of people involved remains low. The European Centre for Disease Prevention and Control reports that, "in 2008, 25,656 HIV cases were diagnosed and reported by 27 European Union and EEA/EFTA Member States (excluding

Austria, Denmark and Liechtenstein), a rate of 5.7 per 100,000 ."[7] The total number of those living with HIV in Western and Central Europe is estimated at 620,000, i.e. 0.2.[8] That such a low rate of infection has been achieved without compulsory measures is the most compelling evidence that compulsory testing for HIV is unwarranted. This may be different in countries of Sub-Saharan Africa where the rate is high as, for example in Swaziland where it is as high as 25.9% Fortunately the global HIV rate in Sub-Saharan Africa is falling among adults (ages 15–49).[9]

Other means of lowering the rate of infectionare possible and have been attempted in other societies. In Cuba those found infected after mandatory testing from 1986 to 1993, were quarantined. The Cuban health authorities subsequently permitted infected individuals to live outside the sanatoria, when considered responsible. Cuban health authorities also "actively pursue contact tracing and HIV testing of sexual partners."[10] This results in the lowest HIV infection rate in the world. As one Jewish cholar has pointed out, a community could pass protective legislation as a preventive measure (Isserles, *Shulhan Arukh, Hoshen Mishpat* 427:1) It is unlikely that we would be prepared to take such measures, even if we find precedence in the *halakhah* Because the incubation period for HIV is long, repeated testing would be necessay.

We have limited our discussion to those living within a certain state, and have not dealt with it as a mandatory requirement for immigrants. One might consider such measures warranted for those entering from countries with a high HIV rate. The International Task Team on HIV-related Travel Restrictions of the UN is currently discussing this matter. The defense for such restrictions has stated that generally travel restrictions have no public health justification. HIV is not a public health hazard since the virus cannot be transmitted by casual contact.Restrictive measures may run counter to public health interests, since exclusion of HIV-positive non-nationals adds to the climate of stigma and discrimination against people living with HIV and may thus deter nationals and non-nationals alike from using HIV prevention and care services. Such travel restrictions may encourage nationals to consider HIV a "foreign problem," so that they feel no need to engage in safe behavior themselves.

Travel restrictions have no economic justification because people living with HIV can now lead long and productive working lives; they pose no potential drain on national health resources. Furthermore such treatments are constantly becoming less expensive.[11]

We may ask whether treatment should be forced upon an individual who has tested positive. The tradition would seem to demand it. There is a biblical obligation to maintain health along with the assumption that our body actually belongs to God. These principles would operate even when the medical measures only lengthen life, but do not cure it of disease as with HIV.

From my perspective this should not occur, as it infringes on the individual's autonomy for no good reason. Since there is no cure for HIV, the risk, of transmission remains the same. We might best follow the principle of do nothing (*shev v'al ta-ase*).

Mandatory testing might be relevant in the compulsory testing of everyone that enters a health care setting. Mandatory as opposed to opt-out testing would make sense only, if the physician could refuse treatment to such an individual. Since the risk of becoming infected with HIV in a health care setting is very small, it would constitute only a doubtful danger (*safek sakana*), so no treatment should be demanded.[12]

For all these reasons there is no need for compulsory testing for HIV, though opt-out screening would be acceptable.

Notes

1. http://www.ft.com/cms/s/0/0485c2ec-d3f8-11da-b2f3-
0000779e2340.html?nclick_check=1.

2.. http://www.cdc.gov/hiv/topics/testing/index.htm. These recommendations seem
to have alreadybeen implemented by some states. For instance the State of New
Jersey, has enacted a law to implement routine opt-out screening for all pregnant
women (http://biotech.law.lsu.edu/cases/STDs/4218_R2.pdf).

3. S Deichowsky "Compulsory Testing and Treatment for AIDS" in G. Freudenthal
(ed.) *AIDS in Jewish Thought and Law* (Hoboken, N.J. 1998), p. 105.

4. G. Freundenthal "Introduction" in G. Freudenthal (ed.) *AIDS in Jewish Thought
and Law,* p. xxxviii.f..

5. M. Halprin, A. Steinberg "AIDS – Reward and punishment and compulsory
testing – Remarks to the Reply" (Heb.) found at:
http://www.medethics.org.il/articles/ASSIA/ASSIA61-62/ASSIA61-62.14.asp.

6. D. Golinkin, "Responsa Regarding the Assassination of Prime Minister Yitzhak
Rabin z"l in *Responsa of the Va'ad Halakhah of the 'Rabbinical Assembly of Israel*
(Jerusalem 1998), Vol. 6, p. 314 f.

7. http://ecdc.europa.eu/pdf/ECDC_epi_report_2007.pdf, p. 44.

8. UNAIDS Report on the Global Epidemic | 2010
(20101123_GlobalReport_full_en.pdf), p. 188.

9. Ibid., 181.

10. http://www.thebody.com/content/art32967.html.

11.http://www.unaids.org/en/KnowledgeCentre/Resources/FeatureStories/archive/20
08/20080304_HIVrelated_travel_restrictions.asp

12. To such cf. for an extensive treatment of the subject: J. Roth, "Organ Donation:
Part IV: Live Donors - Kidneys" in K. Abelson, D.J. Fine (eds.) *Responsa 1991 –
2000* (New York 2002), p. 256 ff.

CHANGING VIEWS OF HEALTH CARE DELIVERY
The Individual versus the Community
Walter Jacob

Every person is entitled to adequate food, shelter, education, and personal security is a common present day assertion The recent American debate demanded that we add medical care to this list. It was framed in terms of government responsibility versus that of the individual, a question that could not have been posed in a simpler, poorer society, nor before our era of continual medical progress. The legislation of universal health care has settled this question with considerable acrimony. It has, however, not ended the debate over individual responsibility versus communal obligation that remains very much with us.

Decades of debate preceded even incremental steps from total individualism to social obligation. We began with charitable efforts and humanitarian concerns prompted by the danger of disease to the broader community. As this did not solve the problem, we provided limited medical care for the poor through Medicaid. The aged represented another concern, their care was served through Medicare. Universal health care represents a further step again taken only over vigorous opposition.

The division of opinions over the responsibility of the individual and the community remains. This paper is written on the premise that a comparable efforts to solve a major community wide problem may not only be found in contemporary European health care models, but also in the Jewish past. The Jewish tradition has dealt with a similar issue through the centuries not in the area of health care, but with poverty. The slow evolution from appeals to individual conscience to communal legislation provides a good model from the past.

Why did the Jewish tradition not follow the path so

successful in the struggle against poverty with health care? Health care in earlier times was simple and limited. The complex procedures which have been developed in the last decades did not exist. A physician could help, but within clearly defined limits and such care was given to rich and poor alike. The great philosopher physician Moses Maimonides set an example along with hundreds of others before and after him. Medical expenses were limited, therefore individual *tzedakah* could take care of poor patients. The Jewish communities sometimes also became involved through paying for the education of a young man who would return and serve his home town a its physician. No complex system of dealing with the problem of health care was necessary. By the time it was needed Jewish self-government had dissolved as Jews became part of the modern state. Most larger Jewish communities established Jewish hospitals in the nineteenth and twentieth centuries which cared for the indigent and also provided a setting where Jewish physicians could practice as they were excluded from other hospitals. These Jewish hospitals were abandoned or became part of national systems when health care was nationalized in much of Europe and for other reasons in North America. Had the open society in which Jews are full and equal citizens not developed, the Jewish community would probably have followed the path used for dealing with poverty and moved from individual responsibility to communal concerns. We will trace the slow development of this path through the ages as it may influence our current thinking.

The Jewish premise of the supreme value of every human life provided the basis upon which concern for poverty and now health care rests. The Bible sees human life as a divine gift (Job 33:4), and Judaism equates each life to the divine initial act of creation. Each human being is to be viewed as similar to Adam and Eve, the first indispensable human beings, so no human life may be damaged, destroyed, or hastened toward death in any way (Shab 151b; A.Z. 18a). Saving a single life, therefore has been understood as akin to saving the entire world (B.B. 10a). This primary obligation is listed among the positive commandments assembled in the Talmud and later writings.

As such supreme value has been placed on human life, the physician's work of healing has always been understood as a *mitzvah* and as assistance to God's initial act. It has never been seen as interference with God's intentions (B.K. 85a; *Bet Yosef* to *Tur* Yore Deah 336). No ritual obligation was permitted to stand in the way of the healing process, not the holiness of the Sabbath or anything else.

Parallel to this is the view that life be lived fully; life and love were celebrated in the biblical *Song of Songs*. Life should be thoroughly enjoyed. The broad implications were clearly stated in biblical times through the regulations governing military service stipulated in Deuteronomy. As such service always endangered life, individuals were excused from military service if they had not yet fully enjoyed some of the basics of human life, including a new wife, a new house, and even a new vineyard. Any of these eliminated the obligation of military service with its inherent danger of death or injury (Deut 20:5 ff. and commentaries; *Tur* and *Shulhan Arukh*) Maimonides further elaborated on these conditions and broadened their application (*Hillkhot Melakhim* 5:1 ff).[1]

Discussions in post-biblical Judaism indicate that the command to save human life is understood in a very broad context; every human life was included, no matter what the cost or the difficulty. This applied to all human beings irrespective of religion, race, or any other consideration. Saving a human life overrides virtually all other commandments. This became clearest in the well developed discussions of the *Shabbat* regulations and their prohibition of every conceivable form of labor. Any act connected with saving a human life, or rescuing someone from a life-threatening danger was excluded (Yoma 85b; *Tur* and *Shulhan Arukh, Orah Hayyim* 329.3).[2] All such actions were obligatory. These and other parallel statements are equally applicable to modern universal medical care.

MEDICAL INTERVENTION

The effort to preserve and improve human life has always included medical care. As life is a divine gift, it must be helped in every way possible. The best medical care available was always seen as a personal obligation. Such efforts were praised through the millennia, included in every compendium of the *halakhah* from early times onward and rarely questioned, so the apocryphal Book of Ben Sirach devotes the entire chapter thirty-eight to this theme. When the tradition discussed experimental treatments, it weighed the potential benefit of the treatment against the *sakanah* (danger). Whichever was more likely to save a life was not only permitted, but encouraged (Ber 3a; Shab 32a; Hul 10a; *Yad Hil. Hovel Umazik* 5:1). These discussions continued through the centuries and have set the pattern for contemporary Jewish physicians.

The value of human life is paramount, and the demand was that everything that could be done to sustain it, should be undertaken. The ability to heal may have been considered a divine gift, but its exercise was in human hands. It was also a human task to define its limits and to guarantee that the fruits of such efforts were widely available and that was relatively easy with the simple health care which existed in earlier times.

Health care remained an individual matter with some help

from the medical profession and that took care of the problem. When the focus was on poverty, the Jewish tradition also turned to the individual.

INDIVIDUAL RESPONSIBILITY AND POVERTY

Helping the poor was a *mitzvah* incumbent on every. It was the task of every individual to help the poor. We need to see how the Bible thought it could motivate people in this direction. It began with the individual conscience. Help for the poor is a constant theme through which the biblical texts prompt the individual. We see it in the specific demand in Leviticus not to harden our hearts against our poor brother (Ex. 23:6; Deut. 15:7). Such statements led to prophetic reminders (Is. 3:14; 10:2; 41:17; Jer. 22:16, which linked impending doom of the land to social injustice (Hos. 4.1f; 5.10f; Amos 2:6 ff; 511 f; ; 8:4 f; Micah 2:1; 6:8 ff; Zeph. 1:9 f; Zech. 11:4f; Mal. 3:8f; Is. 1:23f; 3:14; 5:8; 58:2 ff; Jer. 5:25ff; 6:7 ff.; 7: 6ff.; 34:13ff; Ez. 18:5 ff; 22:12 f, 29 f), a major factor second only to idolatry. This is balanced by a vision of social justice (Is. 11:4ff; 41.17ff There are sharp statements in Proverbs and Psalms (12:6 14:4; 35:10ff.; 37:9ff.; 82:3f; 94:3 ff; 113:7 ff.).

All these statements were directed at the individual and emphasized personal religious obligation. Conscience was to be educated and stirred and when that did not succeed, it was linked to the threat of Divine punishment. God would hear their cries (Ps. 113:7; Prov 31.9; Job 5:15); however it was a human duty to hear them also and to help. We should note that the poor were not blamed for their plight; it was not laziness or personal faults that led to their plight. Help to the poor was provided, but never enough to solve the problem.

As individual efforts were insufficient, the Bible turned to a more realistic approach through the practical legislation that demanded that the corner of the fields and the gleanings be left for the poor and the stranger (Lev. 19:9–10; 23:22; Deut. 24:19–21; amplified in Jud. 8.2; Is. 17:5–6; 24:13; Jer. 49:9; Mic. 7:1; Ruth 2:3, where we see that this legislation was indeed followed). This simple system helped the poor and was psychologically effective because it was not a dole: the crops were harvested by the poor and the stranger. These laws represented an entitlement, forced each farmer take the appropriate action and were far reaching. The system seems to have been effective in a simple agricultural setting and solved the problem for the rural poor. It depended, of course, upon the vagaries of the weather and the problems of grain storage. The success of this system along with the need to deal with numerous details can be seen in the legislation of the *Mishnah* and the two *Talmuds*. Much of what has been spelled out there must already have existed as law or custom earlier, as the simple biblical statements provide few details.[3]

Another way of solving a portion of the problem was the tithe; it was initially intended as a gift to God, as exemplified by the young patriarch Jacob who promised one tenth to God (Gen.28:18–22). The later legislation specified that "seed from the ground and fruit from the tree" along with herd and flock were to be tithed (Lev. 27:30 ff). There is some confusion about the use of the tithe, but a portion was designated for the poor.[4]

The tithe was clearly part of Israelite life until the destruction of the Temple. Rabbinic literature, both early and late, especially the *midrashim*, sought to devote it entirely to alleviate poverty. The ideal of providing ten percent of one's income for the poor remained and was important in Judaism as well as later in Christianity. There was considerable talmudic discussion about

how such funds were to be used and that was continued in the
Middle Ages. Efforts were made in later centuries to continue
tithing.[5] The tithe along with other gifts were to be distributed so
that the poor were not shamed.

COMMUNAL EFFORTS OF THE BIBLE

This appeal to the individual conscience was accompanied
by broader communal efforts that consisted of the Sabbatical Year,
and the Jubilee Year. In the seventh year the land was to lie fallow
and rest – the crops of the field, vineyards and olive groves,
whatever grew, were open to use by everyone, the owner of the
field, the poor, and wild animals (Ex 23.10; Lev. 25.2–7). All
debts were to be canceled (Deut 15:1–3) and all male Hebrew
slaves released (Ex 21:2–6); Deuteronomy extended this to
females (Deut. 15:12–18). Jeremiah's protest (34:8–12) showed
that when the people were reminded of these laws by King
Zedekiah, they briefly observed them. Otherwise we hear nothing
of them until the time of the Maccabees (1 Mac. 6:49, 53; 16:14;
Josephus, *Antiquities* xii, 9, 5; 8,1). The Biblical social legislation
was designed to provide a series of second chances for the poor.
The Sabbatical Year would cancel all debts and so provide fairly
quick aid.

As the Sabbatical Year carried enormous societal and
economic implications, it was human nature to negate it. One
effort interpreted the Levitical legislation narrowly, and so voided
them in the Diaspora; after all Leviticus spoke of "your land,"
which was interpreted as restricting this legislation to the Land of
Israel. Even there, competitive economic forces made the laws
concerning the cancellation of debts counterproductive, as no one
would lend close to the Sabbatical Year. Their effect was curtailed
by the *prosbul* ascribed to Hillel; it transferred debts to the court

and prevented the drying up of all sources of credit (M. Shev. 10:4). In this legal transaction one or both parties were required to possess realestate. The *prosbul* was used through a portion of the talmudic period but then the entire idea of the Sabbatical Year fell into disuse. as the *Babylonian Talmud* indicated.

The fact that this was observed at all in a poor peasant society is amazing and demonstrates the power of the goal of social equality. At least one scholar felt that they continued to be observed by some until the 11th century. The best evidence for their observance in the first and second centuries is the detailed discussions of the Mishnah and for a slightly later period in the Jerusalem Talmud. However, some Medieval scholars tried to revive the Sabbatical Year as also, in a modified form, some Orthodox Israeli farmers.[6]

A much more idealistic and original way of dealing with the long-term effects of poverty was the Jubilee Year, a great social leveling mechanism (Lev. 25:10ff). After fifty years, all rural property was to be returned to its original owner, and all those that sold themselves into bondage and their descendants were freed (Lev. 25.10). Urban property was excluded; there is no discussion of the reason for this in the text or later commentaries. This verse proclaims these famous words: "Proclaim liberty throughout the land, unto all the peoples thereof," which we in the United States quote but forget the next section. The fundamental principle undergirding this concept is that the land is inalienable – it belongs to God. This is highly idealistic and was probably never observed. Though the *Book of Jubilees* tried to reawaken this ideal.[7]

The Jubilee would, after a period of fifty years, restore complete equality throughout the society. Everyone would be given a chance to start again. This was a wonderful appealing ideal, but remained as an ideal.

In any case neither the Sabbatical Year nor the Jubilee provided any immediate relief from poverty, however, they may have given long-term hope. Other methods were necessary.

LATER COMMUNAL CONTROLS

We do not know when the ancient Jewish communites decided to intervene in a revolutionary way and assume communal responsibility for the problem of the poor.[8] A quick review of the legislation indicates that it was worked out early in sufficient detail to take care of the problem and to deal with any objections which members of the community might make. The legislation specified minimal support of the poor, which had to consist of enough, so that if sold it would have the value of two meals. This was followed by statements establishing a system that separated the itinerant and local poor but provided for two collections, *tamhui* and *kupah*. along with specifics for their distribution. *Kupah* took care of the longer term needs of the poor on a weekly basis and so dealt with the local poor. The sums were generally distributed on Friday by three officials and were intended to provide fourteen meals, two per day, for an entire week. The necessary funds were collected by two communal officials from anyone who had been in residence for three months. *Gabbai* or *parnas* were the titles used to designate these collectors, so they were leaders of the community. The task was an honor but involved much work and responsibility.

Tamhui consisted of daily collections, which also involved the entire community. This was immediately distributed and largely intended for the itinerant poor; it was a kind of soup kitchen. Collection for it – in kind or money –, was mandatory and was gathered by two communal officials and distributed by three; in other words, the equivalent of a *bet din*. The distribution was considered more difficult than the collection (B.Shab. 118a). These individuals received absolute trust and were not required to present an audit (B.B.B. 9a). Those that did not contribute were subject to fines, whipping, or the ban.

This *Mishnah* in this legislation defined poverty as possessing less than 200 *zuzim* in money or property. The discussions indicated that the details of eligibility had been well worked out. If these funds were pledged to a creditor, for example, or represented a wife's marriage contract, the man was eligible. The poor person was not compelled to sell his house or his clothing; if he received an expensive gift of pottery after he had been accepted as poor, he remained eligible. He was also not considered poor if he had 50 *zuzim* in working capital (Peah 8:8 and 9). These sums dealt with a single individual, not a family unit. This legislation had no foundation of any kind in the Bible although it was followed by a number of general moral injunctions from Scripture.

This section of the *Mishnah* defined poverty and set broad standards for welfare that were to endure through the centuries. It dealt with itinerants and local poor. This revolutionary system was presented as if it had always existed and became the foundation of all future poor relief. We may speculate about dating this revolutionary approach, but the texts provide no hints. The talmudic discussion provide further detail, but never question the basic premise, the need for communal action, an appropriate model for governmental efforts in our time.

As food shortages were common, these decisions were

enforced through communal *takanot* that went into great detail including the confiscation of food stock, punishment for hoarding, etc.[9] The medieval Jewish community accepted this mandate to alleviate poverty. Although some efforts were undertaken on an individual basis, most of it was on a communal mandatory level. We see this in the *Sefer Hassidim* with its broad popular appeal and can readily follow it in the influential codifications of Jewish law along with many others. Jacob ben Asher's (d. 1340) *Turim* devoted a section to *tzedakah* and dealt with many details. There were other influential work in the Middle Ages as well and they too treated the details necessary to be effective.

The vast response literature along with communal *takanot*, which dealt with these communal problems through the millenia, constantly return to the issue of wide spread poverty and provide communal solutions which obligated everyone's participation. Communal legislation also dealt with these problems.

MARKET SUPERVISION, PRICE CONTROL, AND RATIONING

This legislation was, of course, not confined to one issue, but regulated many other financial dealings of those that lived in the community as well as new settlers as it was concerned with the broader welfare of the community. Such legislation always demonstrates a keen awareness of the broader implications from excessive or unfair competition or its restriction. It began with the demands of the Torah and the prophetic books for market supervision of weights and measures was well as some price controls. Price controls were established in talmudic times.[10]

The legislation extended further to the storage of necessities which were collected and distributed by three individuals who were above suspicion (*Jer.* Peah 8:7). Contributions could be compelled

(*Tur* and *Shulhan Arukh* Yoreh Deah 248:1; *Sefer Hassidim* 911, 914, 195).

We must remember that Jewish communities functioned as semi-independent units within the broader community in which they existed, whether Christian or Muslim. The Gentile state always considered this as the simplest way to deal with this minority. There were no objections to such legislation or to the prohibition of hoarding export in times of need, (*Shulhan Arukh Hoshen Mishpat* 231:20;(B.B. 90b; *Yad Hil. Mekhirah* 14:5, 8; *Shulhan Arukh Hoshen Mishpat* 231.24, 26) or cornering the market. The distribution of essentials could be mandated in times of need (B.M. 11:27). The legislation took many economic factors into consideration, always with an eye toward ensuring the basic needs of the community.[11]

Towns and larger jurisdictions also regulated associations of merchants or crafts and their pricing agreements as they could affect the living expenses of the general population. This system depended on a well organized Jewish community and often on the permission of the non-Jewish ruler to establish it along with its personnel (*Pinkas Medinat Lit # 741* (1629) dealt with such a system.[12]

When price controls were ineffective or could not be enforced, other methods were used by communal leaders to curtail later abuses, though recognized as second best.

CONCLUSIONS
As long as the Jewish communities formed a self-governing enclave within the broader Gentile state, communal rules for the broader welfare of the community were enforced. The power of the community and its officials was recognized within the community

and by the non-Jewish state. The good will and tzedakah efforts of the individuals was recognized and encouraged, but the community did not rely on it.

The underlying philosophy of this well established system dealt with both the individual and the broader society. Ideally, individuals should be motivated to care for everyone in the community – certainly the basics such as food, shelter, health, and security. The call for justice is clear from the biblical period onward. The weakness of human nature was recognized early, however, and responsibility was shifted to the broader community. The system developed and became more complex as needed and in accordance with the ability of the community. The debate over individual responsibility ceased when suffering demonstrated new needs as our concern with universal medical care.

Although the problems of hunger and decent shelter have not been completely solved even in our wealthy western societies,we are closer than any generation before us. For a vast segment of the population, the primary issue now is a reasonable level of health care – delivered in a way that is not degrading and that is provided to everyone. This is certainly possible, but will not occur if left to individual or corporate conscience. What we have described in this paper dealt with the idealistic efforts from biblical times through the centuries; some appealed to individual conscience while others sought communal concurrence. All failed, but practical communal ordinances, rigorously enforced through police poweers succeeded. Poverty may not have been eliminated, but a basic standard of living existed. The wealthy grumbled as always, but they managed well nevertheless.

The same model can be applied to universal medical care. If the Jewish community were self-governing and had the status of a 'state within a state' as was the case for almost two thousand years, it would certainly have followed the model which worked so well with the problem of poverty.

For us as part of the larger community and committed to it, the changing Jewish efforts through the centuries provide a good test of how to reach goals which are necessary, but sometimes appear impossible. Individual efforts cannot provide solutions for some problems, but the community together may succeed.

Notes

1. Such requirements represented an ideal that no state easily tolerated, as we see in the case of King Asa (I K. 15:22), who permitted no exemptions; something probably done by other Jewish rulers as well. This historical record, however, indicated that the biblical injunction was widely known and had to be taken seriously, even if not followed.

2. The question of priority, that is which life shall be saved, naturally arose and was put vividly through an anecdote of a stitutation in which it was not possible to save two lives. This well- known talmudic tale described the dilemma faced by two traveling merchants lost in the desert with sufficient water for the survival of only one. In the discussion one of the scholars, Ben Petura, stated that they should share the water and face common death. R. Akivah, however, rejected that conclusion and stated that each party was obligated to struggle to survive (B.M. 62a). Although no decision was reached in this discussion, it became clear that one death was preferable to two.

3. The tractate, *Peah*, which was concerned with the problem of poverty began with ethical encouragement, then continued in a practical vein with specifics. The farmer was liable for at least 1/60 of his crop, although there was no limit and all depended on the size of the field, the number of the poor, and his generosity (Peah 1.2). "Everything which is food, stored, and grows from the ground (excluding mushrooms, for example) and gathered at the same time (so that figs and olives which were harvested at various times were excluded), and placed into storage (greens are exempt) and grains as well as pulse (beans and peas) were subject to these laws" (Peah 1:4). The law included trees and enumerated "carob, nuts, almonds, vines, pomegranates, olives, date palms" (Peah 1:5). What could be

gleaned as well as definitions of "forgotten sheaves" were provided (Peah 7) along with "droppings" (Peah 4.10). What constituted a field was specified, as were fields with mixed crops, partnerships, undivided estates, and so on. The farmer could not hide gleanings under a bundle of grain; when winds blew the gleanings away, an estimate of what should have been left was mandated (Peah 5:1). Such details and others demonstrated an effort to be fair and not to permit the natural inclination to minimize this tax to prevail.

The law took into account the peculiarities of the vine and date palm harvest and permitted the farmer to harvest and distribute the fruit rather than let it be gathered by the poor; if poor person, wished to harvest it themselves, however, permission had to be given (Peah 4.1, 2).

The farmer was protected against excessive crowding of the fields by limiting gleaning to three times per day. The gleaners were protected by an ordinance that forbade anything that could be used as a weapon from being taken into the field (Peah 4.4, 5). The farmer could not favor one poor person over another; the gleanings were on a "first come" basis (Peah 4:9), nor could he set it aside for his relatives (Peah 4:3). Special provisions were made for the elderly and weak among the poor (Peah 8.1). If there was doubt whether a gleaner was actually poor, he was initially believed and questioned later (Peah 8.2). The itinerant poor were permitted to glean (Peah 5.4) with a division of opinion of whether they should make restitution upon returning home (Peah 5.4) *Mishnah* Peah concluded, as it had begun, with a set of moral injunctions as at the beginning.

4. One text indicated that it was to be "consumed in the presence of God," in other words used for pilgrimage to Jerusalem (Deut. 14:22ff), but every third year it was to be given to the Levites (Deut. 14:27ff.). Another verse specified that it was for the poor and the Levite in the third year (Deut 26:12). A different text indicated that the tithe was simply for the Levites (Nu. 18:21), as the priests received first fruit along with other gifts that could be used to maintain the sanctuary.

A second tithe provided occasional funds to the poor, but it was primarily used for pilgrimages to Jerusalem. Only in the second and sixth year of a seven-year cycle was it given to the poor.

Tithes were mentioned in 2 Chronicles. (31:2–12) but in none of the other later books. Details of the system of tithing were provided by two tractates of the *Mishnah* and in the *Jerusalem Talmud,* but as these laws applied only to the Land of Israel, they were academic, for a high percentage of the world Jewish population by that time lived in the Diaspora. The prophets sought to extend the obligation to Babylonia and the early rabbis to Egypt and the neighboring lands (Demai 6:11), but we do not know with how much success.

5. The scholarly family of Asher ben Yehiel (1250–1327) set a fine example in Toledo where they resided after moving from Germany. They signed a statement through which they accepted their father's ordinance, which obligated them and their children to provide a tithe of all their profits to the poor and agreed to pay it within eight days of the due date. The example of this leading family and others led to the tithe becoming fairly universal. Israel Abrahams, *Jewish Life in the Middle Ages* (London, Edward Goldstone: 1932), pp. 344 f.

6. Asher ben Yehiel in 12th-century Spain tried to revive the practice, but with little success. A small group of farmers in modern Israel follow the segment of the law that demands that the land lie fallow; some use hydroponics to circumvent the letter of the law but voiding its spirit.

7. The *Book of Jubilees* (200 B.C.E.–100 C.E.) attempted to recreate the history of the patriarchal period by reorganizing it in fifty-year periods. *Jubilees* was not included in the canon and remained forgotten until the nineteenth century, when one complete manuscript along with some fragments were discovered.

8. The legislation appeared in the mishnaic section, Peah, chapter 8. which dealt with 'gleaning' and without any connection to that earlier system. No Scriptural source was given.

9. Louis Finkelstein, *Jewish Self-Government in the Middle Ages*, New York, 1964 is the most accessible source.

10. Market officers who looked after fair weights and measures also dealt with prices (B.B. 89a). As in our times, the recorded discussion indicates some opposition to any controls (B.B. 99a). It depended ultimately on the Exilarch for enforcement (J. *Talmud*, B.B.5.5;15a). Price controls usually occurred on the local level in the talmudic period (B.M. Tosefta 11.23); the townspeople had the authority to set prices as well as workers' wages. They were also authorized to compel the local citizenery to build a synagogue, furnish it and obtain a Torah. Those who objected would be fined. Price controls applied to necessities – oil and flour; luxury items were not affected.

The later codes show that a profit level for essential goods was generally accepted, so Maimonides (1135–1204), (*Yad, Hil. Mekhirah* 14.1), and Karo (1488–1575); *S.A. Hoshen Mishpat* 231.20) limited the profits to 1/6th as we have previously stated. All also prohibited hoarding which was already done by R. Samuel (B.B. 90a).

11. Profit margins, which had been set in the 4th century as by R. Samuel with a markup of 1/6th; this remained enforced through the centuries (B.B. 90a; Ahai Gaon, *Sheiltot* 32; *Yad Hilhot Mekhirah* 14:1; *Shulhan Arukh Hoshen Mishpat* 231:20)). The effect of lowering the price was taken into consideration before such action was taken – would it help the consumer or destroy the market place ? (B.B. 91a). When price fixing occurred it needed the approval of communal officials (Tosefta B.M. 11:23).

Some legislation was local, but in other areas national synods passed legislation that dealt with profit margins, tax rates, and appointed officers to supervise and deal with problems (Louis Finkelstein, *The Synod of Frankfort*, 1603, 257 ff. - as an example). Some *takkanot* as those of Italy (1416–1418) dealt with copyright (ibid., 304 ff.), and others placed limits on monopolies

12. The *Shulhan Arukh* stipulated (*Hoshen Mishpat* 231.28) that crafts and merchants could reach such an agreement; however, if it affected a large community the communal leader had to approve it. This continued to be followed later, and there were numerous prohibitions against selling at exorbitant prices. Such agreements were restricted(Meir, *Bet Habehirah* to B.B. 9a) and had to be approved by a"distinguished person" (Ramban, *Hidushei Ritbah* to B.B. 9a).

When the entire community was affected, such legislation was permitted. (Isaac B. Jacob Alfasi (Algeria 1013–1103) Responsa 13 (ed. Leiter), Solomon Adret (Spain 1235–1310) vol 2 #279; Vol. 5 # 126, 270, 242). Levine p. 99). Such legislation with citations from the traditional literature has been passed by the State of Israel through the years including a "Consumer Protection Law" in 1980–1981.

SELECTED REFORM RESPONSA

The responsa on the following pages represent a selection taken from a century of American Reform responsa. They have answered questions from members of the Reform community and its rabbis. We are grateful to the Central Conference of American Rabbis Press for permission to republish these responsa. They have been presented as previously published with no effort to change the Hebrew transliteration or their style; minor corrections have been made.

Additional large selections of responsa on medical and health related issues may be found in the volumes *The Fetus and Fertility in Jewish Law – Essays and Responsa* and *Death and Euthanasia – in Jewish Law – Essays and Responsa.*

DANGERS OF SURGERY
CORRECTING CONGENITAL CRANIOFACIAL
MALFORMATIONS

QUESTION: A twenty-six year old man was born with Apert's syndrome, a disorder which is known as craniofacial dysostosis. This illness is found in a severe form in my patient, Albert. His strange appearance frightens children. He cannot chew food properly. His nasal airway is small, so he cannot breathe through his nose. He is disturbed and he suffers from many colds, etc. due to poor breathing. Surgery would correct some of these problems and improve his appearance. A social service agency favors surgery and would pay for it.

It is not entirely clear whether this individual wishes to have the surgery. His intelligence is limited as he is educably retarded. His mother is very much dependent on him for companionship and transportation, and has cared for him all his life. The risks of the operation are formidable and might lead to blindness, meningitis, seizure disorder and coma, or even death. The issues in this situation are the following: Albert, due to his limited intellect and his long standing physical deformity, may experience little impact from this extensive surgery and its attendant risks. In addition, the potential sacrifice and suffering the mother will experience are also disquieting. Finally, the expenses to achieve this result will be tens of thousands of dollars, and perhaps more if there are complications. Is it appropriate to proceed? (Dr. L. Hurwitz, Pittsburgh, Pa.)

ANSWER: A number of different questions have been raised by this case. The first is the extent to which one should risk someone's life for an operation whose results, because they are principally psychological, will not be known in advance. The social agency, which will pay for the extensive surgical procedure, feels that it will be beneficial. However, the patient and his mother have their doubts, each for different reasons.

Jewish tradition indicates that one should not wound one's self or endanger one's life. In fact, it stipulates that an individual should remove all possible dangers from himself (Deut. 4.9; 4. 15; Ber. 32b; B K 91b, *Yad* Hil. Rotzeah Ushemirat Hanefesh 11.4; Hil.

Shevuot 5.57; Hil. Hovel Umaziq 5.1). However, later responsa agree that even if there is considerable risk in the surgical procedure, it may be taken if there is a small chance that a cure will be effected (Jacob Reisher, *Shevut Yaakoq*, III 75; Hayim Grodzinski *Ahiezer,* Yoreh Deah 16). The recent Chief Rabbi of Israel, Untermann, sanctioned such an operation solely on the grounds that the chance of success was greater than possible failure (Address to the Congress of Oral Law, Jerusalem, August, 1968; several articles in *Noam* have also discussed this matter (Vol. 12, 13, etc).

The patient may, therefore, undergo the operation even if the risk involved is considerable as long as some medical benefit is likely.

The second question deals with the relationship of mother and child. What role should this play in our decision? We shall view this first from the point of view of the child's continued responsibilities to his parent. There is considerable discussion in the traditional literature on this matter. It deals with two aspects of a child's responsibility toward parents. One is the fiscal responsibility. This rests upon children generally, but of course, not in this case. The other aspect deals with the emotional dependence of the parents upon the child. Conflict in this area often became acute when an adult child moved away from his parents for marriage or another reason. Our tradition stressed the child's independence through comments in biblical tales that dealt with this theme, as for example Genesis 2.24, "Therefore shall a man leave his father and his mother...," and on God's command to Abraham, "Get yourself out of your country and from your family and from your father's house..." (Gen. 12.1). The rabbinic interpretation of these citations provided for independence of the child from his parents, although the rabbis felt the need to defend Abraham (M Ber., 6.4; *Genesis Rabbah,* II p. 369). The medieval *Sefer Hassidim* stated that any son who had made financial provisions for his parents was free to move (#564, p. 371). When dealing with a sick parent, or one who was mentally incapacitated, there was a difference of opinion between Maimonides and Rabad. Both agreed that the son may need to leave the parents, but Rabad felt that the obligation of emotional support remained with the son (*Derishah* to *Tur* Yoreh Deah 240). The *Shulhan Arukh* followed Maimonides in this matter (Yoreh Deah

240.10). Clearly the son remains responsible for the physical and mental welfare of his parents unless an extraordinary difficult situation makes this impossible.

The normal situation of a child leaving a home in order to marry presents potential problems. It is a *mitzvah* for a father to ensure the marriage of his children (Kid. 29a ff; Ket. 52b; San 93a). We will not consider the matter of choice of mate, which has been discussed at great length in the literature. Marriage, with the normal move from the original home, is considered a *mitzvah* (Kid. 29a), and the traditional literature insists that a father is obligated to guide the child toward independence. In our case, the mother is similarly dutybound to ensure her son's independence, or at least to take him as far as possible. He, in turn, must continue to support his mother emotionally and help her according to his ability. The mother's fear of the child's independence should not be a factor in any decision about this operation.

The third issue concerns the resources to be expended upon this individual. The social agency obviously feels that the money spent in this fashion will enable him to be less of a public charge both now and later in life. Jewish tradition lauds expenditures for this purpose. When Maimonides listed degrees of charity, the highest prepared the individual to be independent (*Yad* Hil. Matnat Aniyim, 10.7 ff).

Some doubts have been expressed whether the individual involved would actually be able to benefit from the operation and make the psychological adjustment to his new, improved status. That clearly is a matter of judgment that only a physician with considerable experience can decide. However, the surgeon should see himself primarily as the agent that sets the stage for possible future improvement. Unless this has been done, no improvement is possible. This willingness to take a chance and to risk failure is a basis of many aspects of life and religious life. For example, the entire notion of atonement connected with the *yamim naraim,* and especially *Yom Kippur*, suggests that we may be forgiven for past errors and begin anew; yet, there is no guarantee of such improvement. True repentance is sought, but the goal remains ellusive (Yom. 86b; *Yad* Hil. Teshuvah 1.1 ff).

Tradition would have us note the problems connected with this operation. However, if the surgeon feels that it will be successful, and beneficial to the patient then the risk should be taken.

February 1984

Walter Jacob, *Contemporary American Reform Responsa,* Central Conference of American Rabbis, New York, 1987, pp. 128 ff.

BANKS FOR HUMAN ORGANS

QUESTION: Is there any objection to the establishment of repositories for organs like kidneys, heart, liver, cornea, and segments of skin, so that they can be used to help victims at the proper time? It is now possible to store organs only for a short period. Would Reform Judaism object to long term storage as it becomes feasible in order to save lives? Skin banks now help burn victims survive (Rabbi M. Beifield, Jr., Raleigh, N.C.)

ANSWER: Tradition has demanded the quickest possible burial of the dead and considers it shameful to leave a body unburied overnight unless the delay is for the honor of the dead (Deut. 21.23; San. 46b; M.K. 22a; *Shulhan Arukh* Yoreh Deah 357.1). Burial according to the talmudic discussion in *Sanhedrin* is an act of atonement and also prevents any dishonor to the corpse. The thought of atonement through burial is based on the biblical verse, "And he makes atonement for the land of his people." In other words, burial in the earth will make atonement for the individual (Deut. 32.43). In addition it prevents the ritual impurity of the priests *(kohanim)* who are to have no contact with the dead (Lev. 21.2 ff; *Shulhan Arukh* Yoreh Deah 373.7 f; Greenwald, *Kol Bo Al Avelut,* pp. 249 ff).

Burial of limbs is carried out by extension and was known by talmudic sources (Ket. 20b). Almost all authorities that discuss burial of limbs, however, indicate that it is done only to prevent ritual impurity of the *kohanim* (M. Eduyot 63), and that the other two motivations for general burial i.e. (*Yad* Hil. Tumat Hamet 2.3), atonement and the honor of the dead, are not applicable (Jacob Reisher, *Shevut Yaaqov,* Vol. II #101; Ezekiel Landau, *Noda Biyehudah*, Vol II, Yoreh Deah #209). Maimonides limited the possibility of ritual impurity to a limb that had been completely preserved with skin, sinew, and so on. He felt that other sections of the human body like liver, stomach, or kidneys, did not transmit ritual uncleanliness (*Yad* Hil. Tumat Hamlet 2.3).

It is clear from this discussion as well as recent response that there is no obligation to bury the vital internal organs as they do not transmit ritual uncleanliness. That is true for traditional

Jews, and of course, for us as Reform Jews. As the *kohanim* have no special status among us, the precautions connected with them have no significance for us.

There are no problems about the removal of the organs, but we must now attempt to define the turning point when "independent life" has ceased and can best do so by looking carefully at the traditional Jewish and modern medical criteria of death. The traditional criteria were based on a lack of respiratory activity and heart beat (M. Yoma 8.5; *Yad* Hil. Shab. 2.19; *Shulhan Arukh* Orah Hayim 329.4). Lack of respiration alone was considered conclusive if the individual lay as quietly as a stone (*Hatam Sofer* Yoreh Deah #38).

All this was discussed at some length in connection with the provision by the *Shulhan Arukh,* that an attempt might be made to save the child of a woman dying in childbirth even on *shabbat,* a knife might be brought to make an incision in the uterus to remove the fetus (*Shulhan Arukh* Yoreh Deah 339.1). If one waited until death was absolutely certain, then the fetus also would be dead.

Absolute certainty of death, according to the halakhic authorities of the last century, had occurred when there had been no movement for at least fifteen minutes (*Gesher Hayim* 1,3, p. 48) or an hour (*Yismah Lev* Yoreh Deah #9) after the halt of respiration and heart beat. On the other hand, a recent Israeli physician, Jacob Levy, has stated that modern methods permit other criteria, and the lack of blood pressure, as well as respiratory activity, should suffice (*Hamayan,* Tamuz 57.31).

This discussion was important in connection with the preparation for burial, as well as other matters. When death was certain, then the preparation for burial must begin immediately (*Hatam Sofer* Yoreh Deah 338; Y. Z. Azulai, *Responsa* Hayim Shaul II, #25). In ancient times, it was considered necessary to examine the grave after a cave burial to be certain that the individual interred had actually died. This was recommended for a period of three days (M. Semahot 8.1). This procedure was not followed after mishnaic times.

In the last years, it has been suggested that Jews accept the criteria of death set by the ad hoc committee of the Harvard Medical School which examined the definition of brain death I 1978 (*Journal of American Medical Association,* Vol. 205, pp. 337 ff). They recommend three criteria: (1) lack of response to external stimuli or to internal need, (2) absence of movement and breathing as observed by physicians over a period of at least one hour, (3) absence of elicitable reflexes, and a fourth criterion to confirm the other three, a flat or isoelectric electroencephalogram. They also suggested that this examination be repeated after an interval of twenty-four hours.

Several Orthodox authorities have accepted these criteria while others have rejected them. Mosheh Feinstein felt they could be accepted along with turning off the respirator briefly to see whether independent breathing was continuing (*Igrot Mosheh Yoreh Deah* II, #174). Moses Tendler has gone somewhat further and has accepted the Harvard criteria *(Journal of American Medical Association,* Vol. 328, #15, pp. 165.1 ff). Although David Bleich *(Hapardes,* Tevet 57.37; Jacob Levy, *Hadarom,* Nisan 57.31, Tishri 57.30; *Noam* 5.30)* vigorously rejected those criteria, we can see that though the question has not been resolved by our Orthodox colleagues, some of them have certainly accepted the recommendations of the Harvard Medical School committee.

We are satisfied that these criteria include those of the older tradition and comply with our concern that life has ended. Therefore, when circulation and respiration continue only through mechanical means as established by the above mentioned tests, then the suffering of the patient and his family may be permitted to cease, as no "natural independent life" functions have been sustained.

1.   Acceptance of total cessation of brain-stem function as a criterion of death in keeping with *halakhic* standards for determining death, provided the Harvard Criteria are met.

2. The Committee expressed confidence in the medical profession's ability to provide needed safeguards and to set proper standards.

3. Our support of this new legislation is necessary to correct the lack of uniformity presently found among hospitals and staff in determining the fact or moment of death. This legislation is, therefore, viewed as a "tightening up" of standards.

4. The neurological definition of death serves an important function in view of the widespread introduction of respiratory-assist technology in hospitals.

5. Radiological methods for determining cessation of blood flow to the brain's respiratory centers are considered a particularly valid test for neurological (i.e., brain-stem) death," (M.D. Tendler, ed., *Medical Ethics,* 5th ed., 1975, with addendum 1981). *Hanaah,* the problem of "benefiting from the dead," has been discussed by Solomon B. Freehof (W. Jacob, American Reform Responsa, #86). A transplant lies outside the scope of what tradition has normally understood as *hanaah*; this potential objection does not exist.

As we view the traditional reluctance in this matter, we feel that the desire to help a fellow human being, especially in these dire circumstances of *piquah nefesh,* is of primary significance. From our liberal understanding of the *Halakhah,* this is the decisive factor. The act of donating organs does honor to the deceased; many of those about to die would gladly forgo any other honor and donate organs for this purpose (Kid. 32; *Shulhan Arukh* Yoreh Deah 364.1, 368.1; Isserles *Responsa* #327). As the donation of an organ will help to save the life of another human being, storage until the time of proper use presents no problem. Progress in the future may raise new issues of use and lead us to reexamine this matter. At the present time we should insist that storage and handling be done with appropriate respect and that the disposal of organs that are not used be done with reverence.

March 1986

Walter Jacob, *Contemporary American Reform Responsa*, Central Conference of American Rabbis, New York, 1987, pp. 128 ff.

AIDS AND FREE NEEDLES FOR DRUG ADDICTS

QUESTION: The spread of AIDS takes place in a number of ways. Among them is through infected needles shared by drug users. Among the suggestions of public health officials has been the providing of free needles for drug users. This somewhat curtails the spread of AIDS. Is it ethical to utilize this method which after all enables drug addicts to continue their habit? Ultimately that habit may be as destructive as AIDS (Leonard Silberman, New York N.Y.).

ANSWER: As noted in some previous responsa there is surprisingly little material in the vast response literature about the use of addictive drugs (W. Jacob, *Contemporary American Reform Responsa* #82). As you have indicated, this is a matter of public policy rather than a specifically Jewish issue. We must ask ourselves what are we trying to accomplish. The free needles may somewhat curtail the spread of AIDS. They do, however, continue the problem of drug abuse and do nothing to help the addict overcome his/her addiction. Can we in good conscience move along this partial path and ignore the larger question of drug addiction and its harm to the individual as well as to the broader society?

The use of drugs whose harmful effect is known has, of course, been prohibited by Jewish law (Pes 113a; Eruv 54a; Nid 30b). No person is to endanger his/her life in any fashion (Deut 4.9; 4.15; Ber 32b; B K 91b; *Yad* Hil Rotzeah Ushemirat Hanefesh 11.4; Hil Shevuot 5.57; Hil Hovel Umazig 5.1). Even the use of experimental drugs whose benefit is uncertain has been permitted reluctantly, and only with the full consent of the ill person and if there is reasonable chance that healing will occur. In this instance an additional factor is created by the involvement of health authorities in the use of drugs. In other words, making it easier for those addicted to continue their habit.

Those considerations are negative and would lead us to a negative conclusion. There is, however, another side to this question. AIDS is a fatal disease for which no cure is now known.

Individuals who suffer from this syndrome can be helped for some time, but eventually death is certain. Use of drugs may also kill, but it is possible to be cured of this habit and only a serious overdose or very long-term use will kill. Most deaths result from side effects of the drugs or crimes connected with drugs. Therefore drugs, although a major evil in our society, are the lesser evil for the individual.

We may therefore defend the providing of free needles to known drug users on the grounds that we are helping them to preserve their lives. They will be less likely to be afflicted by AIDS, and so will not spread this disease to others. Furthermore the possibility of a cure from their drug problems, although unlikely, exists. We may therefore say that to prevent a greater evil we will condone a lesser evil, and we do so on the grounds that saving a life permits anything accept murder and adultery. In this instance the life saving factor becomes predominant, and we would condone, albeit reluctantly, the distribution of free needles for this purpose.

June 1989

Walter Jacob, *Questions and Reform Jewish Answers*, Central Conference of American Rabbis, New York, 1992, pp, 273 f.

TAHARAH **AND AIDS**

QUESTION: At the present time the funeral director of the local Jewish funeral home refuses to permit *taharah* for AIDS victims. Are there circumstances under which *taharah* may be withheld? For example, those who died of dangerous infectious disease or should we insist that he treat AIDS victims like all other dead? (Rabbi Norman M. Cohen, Hopkins, Minn.).

ANSWER: The fact that this question is asked at all indicates the progress of modern medicine in removing the danger of most infectious diseases. Through most of our long history the grave danger of plagues and major epidemics was, of course, recognized even while the danger of infectious diseases was not. Special precautions were occasionally initiated during major epidemics, but those who died from any disease were treated alike and were provided with the same preparation before burial. In fact crises like epidemics and plagues led to the creation of new burial societies and to renewed devotion to proper burial. (I. Abrahams, *Jewish Life in the Middle Ages,* pp. 355 ff). Special burial preparations were made only for those who were murdered or those who died in childbirth (For a summary see J. Grunwald, *Kol Bo al Avelut* p 49 ff; and *Sedei Hemed IV,* Avelut #141).

There was, of course, considerable discussion in the rabbinic literature about the reaction to plagues. Flight from the affected areas was encouraged (*Shulhan Arukh,* Yoreh Deah 116.5; and commentaries; see also J. Preuss, *Biblical and Talmudic Medicine,* pp. 151 ff. Solomon ben Simon Duran *(Responsa Maharil #195)* approached the whole matter from a philosophical point of view and asked whether flight would be successful if an individual had already been destined for death. Isaac Luria devoted an entire chapter to the question *(Yam Shel Shelomo* 6.26). A large number of responsa deal with contagious diseases and ways to escape epidemics (H.J. Zimmels, *Magicians, Theologians, and Doctors,* pp. 99 ff. 193 ff.). Flight was the principal remedy.

Those who were not fortunate enough to escape and died were to be buried in the appropriate manner. It might be possible to throw quicklime on the grave to avoid the spread of the plague (*Shulhan Arukh* Yoreh Deah 374 *Pithei Teshuvah*; Jacob Reischer *Shevut Yaakov* II #97). Furthermore, the laws of mourning could be modified or suspended in these sad times (*Shulhan Arukh* Yoreh Deah 374.11 and commentaries).

Although these modifications were readily undertaken, the basic rites of burial were followed as closely as possible. In other words, there is no doubt that in times of mass deaths, when a large proportion of the community had fled, some normal honors accorded to the dead were no longer possible. Yet there was no question about *taharah* or any matter connected with burial or the preparation for burial.

The local funeral director is obligated to perform *taharah* and to treat AIDS victims as all other dead in accordance with local custom and the specific wishes of the family. The funeral director would be encouraged to take all possible precautions to prevent infection by AIDS.

April 1988

Walter Jacob, *Questions and Reform Jewish Answers*, Central Conference of American Rabbis, New York, 1992, pp. 279 ff.

JEWISH INVOLVEMENT IN GENETIC ENGINEERING

QUESTION: May a Jew genetically alter a mouse or may a Jew use a mouse if it has been genetically engineered by a Gentile? What is the status of animals in Jewish law? (Arthur P. Gershman, Arlington, Va.)

ANSWER: Genetic engineering is a field still in its infancy, but we can expect major advances in this area in the future. At the moment it is possible to introduce permanent genetic changes in plants, animals and human beings. There are many questions about the control that need to be exercised and the dangers that may arise from new, altered, or hitherto unknown, substances formed through these methods. Unusual safeguards have been proposed by the scientific community, national and international agencies. Such caution is wise and we should proceed carefully even when we are dealing with animals. This responsum is not intended to discuss genetic engineering in human beings.

We will, perhaps, begin with the question of the status of animals in relation to human beings and the turn to genetic engineering. The biblical statement in Genesis (2.26) placed people above animals and enabled them to rule them and therefore to use them in any way that seemed appropriate and certainly to save a life *(pikuah nefesh)*. So, for example, cattle could be used for food or for various kinds of work (B M 86b; Hag 3b; Meila 13a; A Z 5b, etc). Consumption or sacrifice was limited to those deemed clean (Lev 11.3 ff); the list included animals, birds, as well as fish. Other animals that were unclean could be used by man in various ways. There were few limits on the manner of catching or housing animals as long as it was humane, so various means of catching birds were discussed in the *Talmud* (B M 42a; *Taanit* 22a; Sab 78b; Ber 9b; etc). Animals that endangered human beings such as wolves and lions could be destroyed (Ber 13a). This was even more true of pestilent insects such as grasshoppers, mosquitoes or scorpions and ants. Crop eating field mice and rats could also be destroyed (*Taanit* 19a; 14a; Sab 121b; M K 6b). The *Midrash* that sought to find a use for some such animals as fleas and mosquitoes stated that they were created in order to plague evil people (*Midrash Rabbah* Vayikra 189).

Animals could be used by man as long as they were treated kindly. It is prohibited to consume a limb from a living animal (B M 32b). An animal that was threshing may not be muzzled; it must be permitted to eat as freely as a human being (Deut 23.25 f; B M 87b, 90a; *Yad Hil* Zekirut 13.3; *Shulhan Arukh* Hoshen Mishpat 338). Furthermore, one should not consider acquiring an animal unless one has the means to feed it (J Ket 4.8),and a person should then feed his animals before feeding himself (Git 62a; *Yad* Hil Avadim 9.8).

Unnecessary pain may not be inflicted on animals (Ex 23.5; B M 32a; *Yad* Hil Rotzeah 13.9; Solomon ben Aderet *Responsa* #252 #257). Some of the medieval scholars who were concerned with the protection of animals felt that those precautions needed to be stricter than with human beings, as animals do not have the intelligence to care for themselves or to take a longer view of matters (*Yad* Hil Zekhirut 13.2; David ibn Zimri *Responsa* I #728; Yair Hayim Bacharach *Havat Yair* #191; *Shulhan Arukh* Hoshen Mishpat 337.2). Biblical law prohibited the killing of a mother with its young (Lev 12.28; Hul 83a; *Yad* Hil Shehitah 13; *Shulhan Arukh* Yoreh Deah 16). The later Jewish codes also insisted that a seller inform a buyer of the relationship between any animals sold so that a mother and its offspring would not be slaughtered together on the same day. A similar kind of provision forbade the taking of both a mother and a chick from the same nest (Deut 12.6; Hul 138b *Shulhan Arukh* Yoreh Deah 292).

Kindness to animals included the lightening of the load from an overburdened animal (Ex 13.5). Domestic animals were required to rest on *shabbat* as human beings (Ex 20.10; 23.12; Deut 5.14). Provisions were made for animal care on *shabbat;* for animals normally milked, arrangements for this to be done by a non-Jew were to be made.. If an animal needed to be rescued it was to be done even on *shabbat* (Shab 128a; *Yad* Hil Shabbat 25.26; 1 *Shulhan Arukh* Orah Hayim 305.19).

We should also note that the castration of animals was prohibited, and this has always been considered as a form of maiming, which was forbidden (*Shelat Yaabetz* 1.11). We may summarize this by relating that our tradition demands kind treatment of animals. They may be used by human beings but not treated cruelly. We should note that the medieval discussion by some Jewish philosophers about the soul of animals was left as a speculative issue.

Now let us deal with genetically induced changes in mice that are to be used as experimental animals. Systemic genetic changes are a recent scientific achievement. The only area that approached this field in the past was controlled breeding. Our tradition had very little to say about breeding animals as long as no attempt was made to do so with unlike species. There was a great interest in maintaining species of both plants and animals separately, based in part on Biblical verses (Lev 19.19; Deut 22.10). An entire section of the *Mishnah* (*Kilaim*) dealt with the problem of sowing various kinds of seeds together, grafting one plant onto another and interbreeding of animals. This segment of the *Mishnah* contains eight chapters that dealt with various kinds of mixtures such as the prohibition against interweaving wool and linen and with the cross-breeding of certain species of animals or plants. The *Mishnah* and *Tosefta Kilaim* indicated a fascination with mixtures and sought to explain the natural world from this perspective. The *Mishnah Kilaim* presented two points of view according to a recent scholarly volume by Avery-Peck. The circle of Yavneh argued that species were to be kept separate, as God created order in the Universe and it was Israel's duty to maintain this separation.

Those of Usha argued that Israel imposed order on the natural world and Israel now had to maintain it. Neither group ultimately included nonedible plants in their scheme. (A.J. Avery-Peck *The Mishnah's Division of Agriculture).*

When the *Mishnah Kilaim* dealt with animals, it was mainly concerned about unlike species harnessed together or interbred. Neither the *Mishnah* nor later Jewish literature prohibited ownership of animals bred in such a manner.   Interest in this subject, however, diminished and so there was no Babylonian Talmud to these chapters of the *Mishnah,* and later discussion of this material is sparse.

The chief biblical section that deals with this issue, aside from the legislation mentioned above, is the story in Genesis in which the young Jacob promised to maintain the flock of Laban and as payment asked for the speckled, spotted, and dark-colored sheep and goats.   He then proceeded to influence the breeding in that direction.   Ostensibly this was done through the placement of shoots of poplar, almond, and plane trees but there has been some speculation that he possessed some knowledge of genetics that helped him to his goal of a large flock.   That theory has been advanced by Judah Fliks ("Yorashah Usvivah Bemaaseh Yaakov Betzon Lavan" *Tehumin,* Vol. III pp. 461 ff). We should note that the Biblical commentators do not single this story out for special comment and to the best of my knowledge do not use it as an example of animal breeding.

There were occasional commentaries like Ramman's that stated that human beings should not change nature as that would imply imperfection in God's creation (Ramban to Lev 19.19). That medieval view was found frequently in church literature. It has not been followed by Jewish thinkers.

Jewish law said nothing about changing the characteristics of a particular species or breed.   Throughout the centuries every effort was made to assist nature and to produce animals suited to specific purposes as well as plants that would yield abundantly. Despite Jewish involvement in agriculture through the centuries, this matter to the best of my knowledge. has not been discussed in the older response literature.   In modern times these efforts have been accelerated through selective breeding and an understanding of the genetic process. Most recently cloning of plant tissues has been used successfully to produce plants that are absolutely true; this method holds great promise as well as potential dangers.

Genetic engineering of plants or animals within a species poses few old *halakhic* problems though it raises many other issues.

Human beings have selectively bred plants and animals since the beginning of herding and agriculture to adapt them to specific human needs and environments. Genetic engineering will vastly accelerate this process. This may eliminate poverty, famine and disease but may also bring scourges and problems that we cannot foresee.

We are standing at the edge of a new scientific era. We certainly wish to utilize the potentials of genetic engineering for the benefit of humanity. That may be partially within our power. It is not within our power to stop the scientific experimentation. The human yearning to understand the divine creation and everything in it as fully as possible cannot be halted, nor can the desire to alleviate the problems of hunger, disease, and poverty.

As we learn more about the nature of genetic engineering we must discuss its moral implications both with regard to animals and human beings. We realize that the line between plants, animals, and human beings is thin and in some ways does not exist at all. So we must proceed with caution. In consort with others we must set limits and provide direction. We have, of course, become especially sensitive to all these issues since the Holocaust and the terrible medical experimentation that occurred then.

We may be ready to accept genetic changes made for medical purposes and experimentation, as *pikuh nefesh* is an overriding consideration (Shab 132a; Yoma 85b; *Tosefta* Shab 17 and Alfas; *Shulhan Arukh* Orah Hayim 328.1; Hatam Sofer *Responsa* Hoshen Mishpat #185). Human life must be saved if it is at all possible and even some pain to animals is permitted for this purpose. Economic reasons, however, could not justify such a course of action. These should always be reviewed carefully.

When dealing with experimental animals we should be quite certain that they are not subjected to pain or used for frivolous reasons, as for example, cosmetic experimentation.

A mouse engineered genetically for a specific set of experiments, which will eventually help human beings, lies within the boundaries of utilizing animals for the benefit of human beings.

Naturally, the humane treatment of the animals in accordance with our tradition must be observed. It would be appropriate for Jews to be involved in this kind of genetic engineering and to use the animals that they themselves have genetically changed.

March 1989

Walter Jacob, *Questions and Reform Jewish Answers*, Central Conference of American Rabbis, New York, 1992, pp. 247 ff.

PATENTING GENETIC ENGINEERING

QUESTION: May genetically engineered changes in a mouse designed for medical experiments be patented? (Arthur Gershman, Arlington, Va.)

ANSWER: The members of the Responsa Committee that discussed this question felt a high degree of discomfort with patenting changes in a living creature. The animal itself should not be patented. An animal, in contrast to a plant, possesses an additional element of the sacred (although the medieval discussion of whether an animal possesses a soul was inconclusive and left to the "days of the Messiah").   According to our tradition, animals possess a special relationship with human beings.

Social policy has led to plant patents. This has protected the livelihood of individuals and made a more abundant human existence possible. Patenting an animal, however, leads us in a direction not conductive to respect for life.   The Holocaust has made us aware of the dangers of dehumanization, the process, that is the genetic change, may be patented but the mouse itself should not be patented.

If we look at patents and the protection they offer within Judaism, we realize that the notion of protecting an idea or a newly created work is fairly new. There were periods in our history when the originator of a new work sought to make it seem old and thereby give it a greater acceptance.   That was true of large anonymous sections of the Bible that have been added to various prophetic books, the apocryphal books, and of such works as the *Zohar*.   In modern times we have sought to protect the creative efforts of individuals. We may link this to the traditional concern for protecting an individual's livelihood. It was always considered important to ensure the livelihood of craftsman, artisans, teachers and tradesmen in the community by limiting the access of others or prohibiting it entirely. This was carefully balanced throughout the ages with a concern for the economic well being of the community and concern about a potential monopoly that might drive prices excessively high (M B M 4.5; B B 21a; Kid59a and commentaries;

Yad Hil Zekia Umatanah 1.14; *Tur* and *Shulhan Arukh* Hoshen Mishpat 156; Meir of Rothenburg Responsa #544; etc).

Even in conjunction with "sacred" areas as the teaching and interpretation of the written and oral law, great care was exercised to protect the jurisdiction and status of rabbis and teachers. Some authorities like Isserlein and Weill permitted competition and felt that it was good for the community (Weill, *Responsa* #151; Isserlein, *Terumat Hadeshen* #128). Israel Isserlein made his decision on the basis of encouraging the study of *Torah*. Some later authorities agreed with them. Many scholars felt that the appointed rabbi of the community had a right to protect his status, both as a teacher and a judge. He could also protect the income from these and other sources (*Avnei Nezer* Yoreh Deah 312.37; *Meshiv Davar* 18, 9; *Hatam Sofer* Hoshen Mishpat #21; *Mayim Amuqim* #70). The *Shulhan Arukh* and its commentaries present both points of view (*Shulhan Arukh* Yoreh Deah 245.18 ff). This equivocation on the part of the medieval authorities was intended to encourage strong scholarly leadership.

Matters changed when the modern rabbinate became a profession and the rabbis' livelihood depended upon services rendered to the congregation. Under these circumstances, it was forbidden to trespass on another rabbi's territory (Moses Sofer *Hatam Sofer* Hoshe Mishpat #21: Yoreh Deah #32; *Meshiv Davar* #8). Some disagreement remained on the right of a newcomer to teach, as this is a *mitzvah* and its fulfillment should not be denied to anyone (Elijah ben Hayim *Mayim Amuqim*, #70; Akiva Eger, Responsa Tanina #12; Abraham Mordecai Halevi *Ginat Veradim* Yoreh Deah 3.7). Livelihoods were protected and the matter under discussion is related to this question.

Similarly books of prayer that were in the public domain and which could be considered part of the divine tradition were protected through copyright. So, for example, the first edition of the famous Heidenheim *Mahzor,* printed by Roedelheim contained statements by four prominent rabbis granting a copyright. When a printer in Sulzbach proceeded to republish the work, a special statement warning against its purchase was issued by Pinhas Horowitz of Frankfurt (final page Heidenheim *Mahzor* 1832).

Many responsa subsequently have dealt with copyrights. The main consideration was the effort and investment made in the work; without protection publishers would be unwilling to undertake such risks (Moses Sofer *Responsa* Hoshen Mishpat #41; etc). All these instances indicate that protection of an invention is permitted and may be considered necessary as well as desirable.

We can see that the pattern of tradition intended to protect someone's livelihood and reflected social policy. As we look at this social policy in connection with medical experiments we must always ask ourselves whether this enhances or diminishes the respect for human life and all life.

In conclusion we have many reservations about patenting an animal and would reject that concept. We also have reservations about the implications of patenting the genetic change. We would tentatively agree to patenting the process.

March 1989

Walter Jacob, *Questions and Reform Jewish Answers*, Central Conference of American Rabbis, New York, 1992, pp. 247 ff.

CONTRIBUTORS

Walter Jacob is President of the Abraham Geiger College in Berlin/Potsdam; Senior Scholar of Rodef Shalom Congregation, Pittsburgh, Pennsylvania; President of the Freehof Institute of Progressive *Halakhah* and Past President of the Central Conference of American Rabbis. Author, editor, or translator of forty books including *Christianity through Jewish Eyes* (1974), *American Reform Responsa* (1983), *Contemporary American Reform Responsa (*1987*), Liberal Judaism and Halakhah* (1988), *The Second Book of the Bible: Exodus Interpreted by Benno Jacob* (1992), *Die Exegese hat das erste Wort* (2002), *The Environment in Jewish Law (*2003*), Pursuing Peace Across the Alleghenies* (2005), *Hesed and Tzedakah – From the Bible to Modernity (*2006*), War and Terrorism in Jewish Law* (2010), Benno Jacob, *Kämpfer und Gelehrter* (2011).

Audrey Korotkin is the rabbi of Temple Beth Israel in Altoona, Pennsylvania. She is a Ph.D. Candidate in rabbinic literature and thought at Hebrew Union College-Jewish Institute of Religion, Cincinnati, Ohio, from which she was ordained in 1999.

Jonah Sievers is the Rabbi of Braunschweig, Germany, President of the Allgemeine Rabbinerkonferenz of Germany, European Chair of the Solomon B. Freehof Institute of Progressive *Halakhah,* editor of the *Jewish Prayer book for Shabbat and Weekdays* (2009), editor of the *Jewish Prayer book for Pesach, Shevuot, and Sukkot* (2011).

Mark Washofsky is the Solomon B. Freehof Professor of Jewish Law, Hebrew Union College – Jewish Institute of Religion in Cincinnati, Ohio; Chair of the Responsa Committee of the Central Conference of American Rabbis; Vice-Chair of the Solomon B. Freehof Institute of Progressive *Halakkah*. He has published numerous studies in the field of Jewish law, legal theory and contemporary ethics. He is the editor of *Teshuvot for the Nineties* (1997), and author of *Jewish Living: A Guide to Contemporary Reform Practice* (2010).